Intensive Care

Intensive Care

Inside An Intensive Care Unit

Dr Paddy Yeoman
and Alan Sleator

B⊞XTREE

A companion to the BBC series 'Intensive Care'

First published in Great Britain in 1995 by
Boxtree Ltd

Text © Dr Paddy Yeoman/Alan Sleator 1995

The right of Dr Paddy Yeoman and Alan Sleator to
be identified as Authors of this Work has been
asserted by them in accordance with the Copyright,
Designs and Patents Act 1988.

1 2 3 4 5 6 7 8 9 10

Typeset by SX Composing Ltd, Rayleigh, Essex
Printed and bound in Great Britain by
Butler & Tanner Ltd, Frome and London

Boxtree Limited
Broadwall House
21 Broadwall
London SE1 9PL

A CIP catalogue entry for this book is
available from the British Library

ISBN 1 7522 1000 9

Cover photographs by Mike Abrahams

To James, Tom and David
and all those who care
wherever they might be.

Acknowledgements

I WOULD LIKE TO THANK Lesley Clark, Teresa Bugoyne and Dr Iaian Farquhar for their advice. Thanks also to Irene Bostock and Tracie Morgan for their assistance preparing the manuscript.

Author's Note

The University Hospital Adult Intensive Care Unit Trust Fund is a registered charity, No. 1019229. It aims to support research and education in the field of critical care medicine. Donations are welcome. They should be sent to the Treasurer, c/o Adult Intensive Care Unit, University Hospital, Nottingham NG7 2UH.

Cheques should be made payable to University Hospital A.I.C.U. Trust Fund.

Contents

Preface

THIS BOOK is not a detached, clinical description of life in an Intensive Care Unit. It is a highly personal account of some of the things I have seen and experienced during my work as clinical director of one of the busiest units in the country.

Some of my colleagues may find it an uncomfortably emotional account. But I think that if they are honest with themselves, they too will admit to having shared similar feelings at some stage in their professional careers.

I have written this book solely from my own perspective, but no Intensive Care Unit depends upon just one person. Instead, our patients recover because of the combined strengths of an entire team of doctors, nurses and other non-medical staff. They also recover because of the support and encouragement their relatives provide.

In order to protect patient confidentiality, I have mentioned no names and changed some of the details of the cases described.

Introduction

IMAGINE YOURSELF TO BE A DOCTOR. Lying on a bed in front of you is a young man with a broken neck. His spinal cord is injured and his body is paralysed. If you don't act quickly, he will certainly die because he is unable to breathe. Yet if you save his life, he may be profoundly handicapped for the rest of his years, unable to speak or move. It's akin to being buried alive, and the life you save could be one of utter fear and misery. It may also blight the existence of an entire family who will have to look after him for many years to come. What would you do? You have thirty seconds to make up your mind.

To make the decision more realistic let us add another factor: a small proportion of people with similarly severe injuries do, against all odds, go on to make an almost full recovery. Instead of being pitifully handicapped, after treatment they regain all of their abilities and are able to resume a normal life with families and friends. It's a remote possibility, but it does happen and this young man might be one of them. Letting him die now will throw away that slim chance. On the other hand, there is a possibility that because he has not had the power to breathe, his brain has already been starved of oxygen and he has indeed been permanently and seriously brain damaged. What do you do – stand there and do nothing, or begin the treatment? You have fifteen seconds left to make up your mind.

In a waiting room nearby, the young man's mother and father sit, overwhelmed by grief, still in shock after being informed by the police of their son's plight. In a moment, you will have to go into that waiting room and explain to them what actions you have taken. Your decision could mean the death of their son. Or you could be about to inflict upon them the greatest catastrophe

1

they will ever face: a boy so handicapped that from this day forth, they will have to subjugate every moment of their waking existence to caring for him. But it could also mean taking action which would restore him in good health to his parents. You have five seconds left.

Time has run out. All eyes are upon you; everyone is waiting for your decision. A silence fills the room. This young man's life rests in your hands. What are you going to do?

This is just one example of the sorts of decisions which have to be taken by those of us who work in an Intensive Care Unit.

I've been doing this job now for over ten years. At the start, I believed that such decisions would get easier with more experience, and that soon I would be able to reduce them to a simple formula based on what had worked before – but I was wrong. With the passing of time, I may have become better at taking the decisions, but making them has remained as difficult as ever. We all wish we had the power to make the right decision every time, but none of us has. There are many decisions I have made with the best intentions, but now bitterly regret.

Years ago, many of the patients in this Intensive Care Unit would simply have died because we wouldn't have known how to go about saving them, but all that has changed and will continue to do so. Now, with proven experience and new techniques in place, we are able to keep more and more critically ill people alive, so that once-fatal conditions are now treatable, albeit with extensive medical intervention. In the majority of cases the benefits are clear-cut, with the survivors going on to resume a full and active life, just like anyone else. Across the country there are countless people who owe their lives to the intensive care they received on this Unit and other units like it: fathers and mothers and loved ones, who are at home again with their children, and children who are still alive to give at least some of the dreams that every parent holds for their young a chance to come true.

In other cases, however, the advantages of the new techniques are less clear, so that although we can provide a person who would once have died with continued life, it may not be a life of any appreciable quality. Long term nursing homes throughout the country have patients who, as a result of intensive therapy, have survived brain injuries so great that they will never have any meaningful existence again – being severely demented or even in a 'persistent vegetative state'. It is easy to see why our critics sometimes accuse those of us who work in intensive care units of keeping the country's social workers and community nurses in full-time occupation.

In such circumstances, we have to ask ourselves whether it would simply have been better for everyone if the patient had been allowed to die in the first place. It's a tough question – hiding our heads in the sand and refusing to consider it would be the easy option. However, that would not be in the patient's best interests, so someone has to take a decision. Few other hospital departments are faced with these dilemmas to such an extent; surgical wards or medical wards have, in the main, the task of treating as many people as possible given finite resources. Deciding to place a patient far down the waiting list may eventually cause a delay which could lead to that person's death – but in months if not years, so the impact of the decision is removed. When we decide not to treat a patient, we know they will probably die within hours. There is a direct connection between decision and effect.

An Intensive Care Unit is no place for empty moral posturing. There is no line management system which allows you to reach harsh conclusions safe in the security of a boardroom, with the knowledge that some minion, and not you, will have to do the dirty work. Here, you have to take the decision and face the consequences, standing by the bedside, just feet away from the person who will be directly affected by your choice. Sometimes it will be a decision to let them die; then comes the task of telling the relatives that you have decided to withdraw treatment from their mother, or father, or sister or daughter.

In the middle of all this, throughout the day, time and time again, other choices have to be made which are no less challenging.

Would you spend £150,000 saving the life of a 72-year-old man, knowing that he will probably die in a few years' time anyway? Each pound spent on his treatment might mean less money available for younger patients with a full life ahead of them. The answer seems simple: it doesn't make economic sense. But would you reach the same decision if that old man was your father? Because he will probably be someone's dad. Could you explain to a crying child that, although she can see her mummy breathe, and can reach out to feel the familiar warmth of her skin, her mummy is already dead? Would would you say?

Medical decisions on an Intensive Care Unit are sometimes difficult, but I find it is the ethical dilemmas which are more difficult still. The most difficult of all is: 'How can I be sure I am doing the right thing.' Medical decisions get easier with increasing knowledge and training, but as the certainty and clarity of youth becomes tempered by experience, each case that I treat provides a different perspective on issues which once seemed so simple to resolve. Who should receive treatment and who should not? What will be the outcome of such treatment and what will be the cost to the patient, their family and society? When should treatment start and, more importantly, when should it end? How far do we go to keep someone alive.

These days we are also forced to make other, some might say unacceptable decisions. How much money should we spend to keep someone alive? Should we discharge one patient from intensive care to make way for another who is younger, or who is even more ill than the seriously ill people already in the Unit. Although it is far removed from medicine, these decisions may also determine who will live and who will die. The prime purpose of an Intensive Care Unit is to treat very seriously ill people and make them better. It brings together unique medical expertise, excellent nursing qualities and the best medical equipment, concentrating them all into one small area to provide, in theory, the best possible medical care. The patients in this unit are generally the most critically ill people in the hospital. Some of the techniques employed here are pioneering. When these two extremes are combined, it is inevitable that an Intensive Care Unit is also a place that sees more than its fair share of medical triumphs and personal tragedies.

We treat victims of the worst car crashes, the most serious industrial accidents, the most crippling illnesses, the most severe head injuries, spinal injuries, suicide attempts, stabbings and shootings. We treat survivors of aircraft crashes, rare killer diseases, drownings, people with multiple organ failure and, if need be, bomb-blast injuries. We also treat patients after complicated surgery who without careful post-operative support would frequently not survive. The crisis cases come here. Saving a life on this Intensive Care Unit costs, on average, roughly the same amount of money as a brand-new basic model Ford Fiesta – about £6,000 a time and this includes the cost of caring for those who die. This is, however, only an average. The cost in some

4

cases may well exceed £100,000. Is it right that so much could be spent to save the life of just one individual? How much is a human life worth? How many more lives could have been saved if this money had been used elsewhere, maybe in less fortunate parts of the world.

Some of the surgery our patients need has to be performed at very short notice. A patient's condition can change in an instant, and medical decisions may have to be taken very quickly. There is often no time to call upon the additional information which can be provided by sophisticated scans and complicated investigations. Doctors have to rely on a mixture of training, previous experience, and simple instinct to reach the correct conclusion, knowing that a wrong choice could kill that patient. By the law of averages alone, we aren't always right.

Working here can sometimes feel like forever being on a downhill ski race. One false move, one mistake and the consequences can be disastrous. Living with such relentless tension and emotional turmoil is never done without high cost. Doctors in general suffer a far higher divorce rate and family breakdown than average and the medical staff in Intensive Care are no exception. Burn-out amongst Intensive Care doctors is quite common, and few Intensive Care nurses continue in the job until retirement. About a quarter of the patients who come to this unit every year will die, despite all of our efforts. For many of the staff here, a high proportion of those deaths will feel like personal bereavements. We see a very distorted view of life.

Relatives who come to this Unit know that they may well be seeing their loved one for the last time. It is a time of intense worry and anguish as they sit by the bedside, not knowing what is going to happen, afraid to leave in case their loved one dies. These aren't the circumstances to encourage jovial, lighthearted conversations. It's an experience which places them too under great pressure, and as a result of such stress, the relatives we see are often in need of a doctor's care themselves. We have rooms where those who have travelled long distances can stay overnight, close to the unit should things take a change for the worse. Sometimes relatives react to the experience of the Intensive Care Unit with anger, violence and bitter words, often aimed at those around them: the medical and nursing teams, who themselves may be coming to terms with a sense of having failed to save that patient's life.

5

Extreme illness often demands extreme methods of combating that illness. Some of the things we are forced to do to our patients make us all question whether we have overstepped the limits of acceptable medical intervention. Is it acceptable to place a 78-year-old woman on a ventilator when it is more than likely that she will spend her final days with a tube down her throat, unable to speak? Is it acceptable to place a patient with progressive vital organ failure on an ever greater number of medical machines at the price of ever increasing discomfort to combat that trend? How do you decide when a patient is really trying to tell you that they want to die? Where do you draw the line? There are no absolutely correct answers – but that doesn't spare us from our duty to find one.

There are as many reasons as people why someone leading a normal life suddenly finds themself in the crisis which bring them through our doors. It can happen in an instant. One teenage girl slapped her boyfriend's face as he drove his car, causing a crash which killed him and left her fighting for her life. Another young man climbed a lamp post in a spirit of festive jollity, only to fall to the ground, sustaining head injuries which later claimed his life. It never ceases to amaze me how death and injury are quite content to arrive during an unguarded moment of trivial existence, or in the midst of happiness and joy as well with in the more customary searing screech and ripping metal of a car crash.

If the disadvantages of working on this unit are extreme so are the rewards. Seeing a patient who should have died, survive thanks to the care and attention provided by this unit, is an overwhelming pleasure. It is also the reason why all of us do the job in the first place, because our success stories far outnumber our failures. Without this colossal benefit, none of us could sustain more than a few months in this place. It is a recipe for the most addictive job in the world, especially for anyone fascinated by human life.

CHAPTER ONE

Chris

THOSE OF US WHO WORK in Intensive Care all have our own personal reasons for doing so. I didn't always want to work in an Intensive Care Unit and I didn't always want to be a doctor.

There was a time when the only thing I wanted to do was to build canoes. Wooden racing canoes, highly polished and sleek, made from mahogany veneer. For several years canoes were my life. I had done quite a bit of white-water work, but my main pleasure as a boy was to paddle down a river with friends and camp on the banks overnight. Making my own boats seemed a natural progression, and I soon became quite good at it.

At first I used ordinary plywood, but soon moved to moulded mahogany. Cutting thin strips of mahogany veneer in the shape of a wish bone, I would slowly construct the craft with resin glue. After the hull, a platter mould would produce the top of the canoe, and at the end of the project I had a smooth, beautifully polished boat, with all the lustre and magic that good quality wood can provide.

Building the boats was great fun, and my skills improved, so that I could make my own designs in mahogany, introducing whatever patterns I wanted to the wood.

Then we received an order for twenty-five racing canoes for South Africa. It was clear that we would either have to build a factory or stop altogether. We just couldn't continue as we were. I was still at school and working on the boats during my spare time. What had started out as a childhood hobby was fast becoming a serious proposition.

But in the end I knew it wasn't for me. Other opportunities in life were only just beginning to open up, and there were so many things that I wanted to do. I had just discovered the joys of rock

7

climbing – a pleasure I have never lost to this very day – and a new interest had taken hold. I wanted to build aeroplanes and I had made up my mind to be a aeronautical engineer. Every aspect of flight and flying was, for me, a definition of absolute freedom. The freedom to soar and swoop, moving effortlessly above the earth in a blue sky with a shining sun was my idea of bliss. I had my future all mapped out when I was just seventeen years old – or so I thought.

My elder brother Chris was nineteen years old, just two years older then me, when he had his motorbike accident. Like many brothers, we weren't particularly close in our early years. When Chris was in his mid-teens, he didn't want to have a younger brother following him around like an irritating puppy dog. I cramped his style, a younger brother still wanting to do younger things. But as each of us grew older we began to share common interests, in mountaineering and canoeing, in music and parties and girls, and doing all the things that boys in their late teens want to do. As those last few years passed, the differences that had existed between us disappeared and we forged a new, strong, close bond. He was, in effect, my new-found friend, someone I could share things with, a companion as well as an older brother.

But all of that ended in August 1969. As Chris was overtaking a van on his motorcycle, the van turned right and he crashed into it, the impact flinging him from his machine straight into a brick wall. He suffered terrible head injuries and stopped breathing at the site of the accident. I suppose he would have died there too, had not a passing policeman seen the accident happen and rushed to give him mouth to mouth resuscitation. It was an act which undoubtedly saved his life. At first he was taken to a local hospital, but he was so critically injured that he was quickly transferred to a neurosurgical centre which specialises in caring for people with head injuries. Doctors there found he had suffered a haemorrhage – bleeding from a burst blood vessel – the blood clot pressing on the base of his brain, starving it of oxygen. Immediately they carried out emergency surgery to remove the clot and stem the flow. There were no brain scans in those days to show the surgeons where to operate. They had to go in blind, following what few clues they could glean from their clinical examination. To this day, I admire their skill.

The first time I saw him was later that night, just after the operation. I was horrified. They had shaved his head; all his long dark hair was gone, and looking at him lying unconscious on the bed conjured up images of concentration camp victims and suffering. Was this really my brother? I could hardly recognise him. What had happened to the carefree spirit I knew and loved? All about me was silence, broken only by my brother's long, laboured breaths. It is a sight and a sound that I have never forgotten.

Although I was seventeen years old, I was still regarded as a schoolboy, too young to be allowed to attend the meeting with the doctor treating my brother. Instead, I was left to wait outside while he spoke to my mother and father, and I remember vividly seeing the effect of what had been said on my parents' faces when they returned from that interview.

Whatever hope my father may have held had been crushed completely by that neurosurgeon. Emerging from that room I saw a broken man, beyond despair. He had just been told that his eldest son would never recover from his profound brain injuries and was probably going to die or, if he were to live, he would certainly be a vegetable. Looking back now, with children of my own, I can just about imagine what it must have felt like to have your hopes and plans, the dreams and aspirations we all hold in our hearts completely destroyed by a few simple words. The blow had fallen heavily, and he was utterly crushed by the news.

My mother, on the other hand, took a different view. Hers was a simple belief: where there is life there is hope. I think my father regarded that as a naive stance. All of his hope had been destroyed, and he could see little point in pretending that a miracle would happen. In the face of harsh reality, hers was a faith my father felt unable to share.

But Chris did not die. Instead, he remained deeply unconscious for months, unable to move, with few active responses, just barely alive. After several months his eyes began to open by themselves, but they would stare into space without the ability to recognise anything. Although he was officially out of coma, there was no sign of consciousness. The correct term for this condition is the Persistent Vegetative State. I hate using it because it sanitizes the offensive word 'vegetable' and in any case no one can tell for certain whether the condition really is persistent. My mother remained hopeful as ever, thinking that surely God would find a way but I could feel my father beginning to wish that she would accept the situation, even when, after nine months, we became aware that he could move his right thumb slightly. A few months later we became sure that he could understand us, and could soon use that movement to indicate yes or no.

At about this time, my father took my younger sister and me on holiday, while my mother stayed at home to visit Chris every day as usual. When we returned, all of us were surprised to find that she had arranged for Chris to come home. There was no point in keeping him at the hospital any longer. He was moved back to the familiar surroundings of our house. From now on, she was to be his full-time nurse. She would fight to save his mind and that's what she did for the next thirteen years.

Chris was very severely handicapped, and looking after him was an onerous task which had to be performed twenty-four hours a day, seven days a week. He needed everything done for him: feeding, washing, shaving, his teeth cleaned, hair combed, enemas to make his bowels function, incontinence devices – the workload was immense. A community nurse would come to help, but the burden still fell heavily on my mother since she was there all of the time.

She believed in sensory stimulation, and although there was no reason to think it would make any difference, each day, she would play records of his favourite pop songs, and classical music that he had loved as a teenager, as well as showing him old photographs and cine films of his childhood. She would talk to him and hold discussions, and treat him with respect as if he was like any other intelligent adult but one unable to respond, because that was how she genuinely felt.

She searched for information. Surely there were experts who knew what to do and who had experience of this sort of situation? There must be people who could give practical help and support, and above all, just a little hope amongst such utter hopelessness. In those days rehabilitation medicine was in its infancy, and few people in the medical profession understood the benefits to be gained from a well planned approach to care at this stage. At best, all she got was sympathy.

Unlike the rest of the family, who don't have religious convictions, my mother has a very strong Christian belief, and it kept her going day after day after hopeless day. She felt certain that Chris was going to survive, and therefore it was up to her to fight for his mind, to give him a quality of life that he would not otherwise have – if she did not do it, no one else would. If, however, he did die, then that too would be a blessing – but only God would decide when that moment of death would come. In the meantime, she had a job to do, and do it she most certainly would. Her zeal was unstoppable. At times, perhaps at the end of yet another long exhausting day without any sign of progress, it must have been a very lonely crusade, for there were few believers, even within her own household. She was clearly regarded as a bit daft by Chris's doctors, who firmly believed that he would never improve. They felt it was a shame that my mother had not come to terms with Chris's vegetative state, and that her endeavours, though brave and caring, could be dismissed as a colossal waste of time.

It was a total disaster for the whole family. For my father it had come at a stage in his life when he could have expected better things. He had successfully endured his fair share of teenage trials from his children, and now was justly looking forward to a bit more freedom and better quality of life. Freedom, perhaps, to return to Africa where we had spent our early years. Freedom to pursue all of the goals, and hobbies and interests that every parent postpones while bringing up a family. Yet none of it was to be. He had learned to accept the horror of the accident but this was agony without end, a dark tunnel with no light to be seen, stretching out across the years of a lifetime.

At the same time, he was trying to hold down a high-powered research job with a pharmaceutical company in a department that demanded results. During those days, I didn't appreciate the pressure he must have been under, trying to think original thoughts and carry out high-quality research programmes with the knowledge that his son was in such a condition. Nor did home provide any respite from the pressure of work. Walking through the door each evening, for ten terrible years, there was no escaping the horror of it all, and no prospect of ever being able to relax. Even now, I still don't feel comfortable asking him to discuss those painful times.

Before the accident my parents were a very close couple; I can remember how they were walking arm in arm, towards the house from the bottom of the garden on that beautiful August evening when the policeman called to tell us what had happened. But in the course of those long hard years after the accident it was clear that the circumstances were testing the strength of their relationship to the limit. My younger sister too, found it difficult to bear. She had been robbed of those carefree teenage years her brothers had enjoyed. Because of her young age she had not been allowed to see Chris at the hospital, and so had not been able to share with us the full reality of the accident.

But incredibly, my mother was proved to be right. Against all odds and medical opinions, Chris continued to improve, and soon he reached a point where it was obvious to us all, even to his medical attendants, that he was very aware of what was being said to him. In those days, most doctors believed that if you didn't make much improvement within the first six months, then you wouldn't make any improvement at all. It is now quite clear that this isn't the case. A small number of brain injured people in a vegetative state do make a small recovery if looked after for a number of years, and an even smaller number make a recovery with some sense of quality attached to it. My brother was among that tiny percentage. The miracle, long prayed for, was beginning to come true.

Chris's improvement continued. Soon he had reached the point where he could communicate by using his finger to outline letters of the alphabet on his chest. Put together, they formed words, a message from a brother who I thought I would never hear from again. It was a moving moment. After all this time, he was speaking to me again, carefully constructing each letter, pausing to recover from the effort, the words nevertheless continued to flow. Here, despite initial appearances, was an active, fully comprehending mind betrayed by a useless body. It's a lesson I have not forgotten to this day when seeing brain injured people.

Slowly, we began to hold conversations. I would ask him questions, and he would write his reply. It was quite laborious, and often he would get tired and his writing would become unclear, and often he would drift into a confused, rambling state. Sometimes, he would get agitated, and have outbursts of rage and frequently use four-letter words. At other times, you could have a sensitive discussion with him about a beautiful painting, and how he loved Picasso. He'd listen to the news and discuss political issues. I remember it was towards the end of the Vietnam war, and he was very upset by what was happening there. All the time, the only real sign of an improvement in an otherwise totally handicapped condition, was this constantly writing finger.

12

At times he would be very entertaining, and strangely enough he retained a sense of humour, which was one of the most obvious things that struck people who hadn't met him before. He could make you laugh, and concoct jokes, some of which were quite elaborate and took a long time to decipher. But at other times he was very down and didn't want to speak about anything. Each message had to cross the barriers of his wretched state, and it was no good pretending that life for him was a sweet untroubled existence. Even now, I can remember the day when, writing very slowly on his chest, letter by letter, he told me that life was an unbearable torment, that he hated being inside his own body and wished he could die. I will never forget it. The fact that he could communicate gave me a rare insight into what it is like to be so profoundly handicapped.

Doctors struggling to keep alive a head injured patient whom they know will inevitably end up profoundly handicapped often debate the quality of life that person will have. It's the old question about whether it would have been better to let them die, or whether there is a joy of existence to be had even in such a restricted state. Usually, there is no definite conclusion other than the doctors' personal opinions, because most profoundly handicapped patients are also too handicapped to be able to tell them.

During Chris's first few days in hospital, there was one doctor, a young neurosurgical registrar, who was kind and considerate. Unlike some of the medical team he had a compassionate approach and continually provided my family and me with the moral support and practical advice that we so desperately needed. He had a calm, reassuring manner and I could see that he was well liked and respected by the other ward staff. He had been the registrar on duty the night that Chris had been admitted. It had been his quick actions that had saved his life. I saw him as a role model, and for the first time I thought that perhaps I should study medicine. The more I talked to him the more convinced I became, and so I decided to scrap my long-cherished plans to build and fly aeroplanes, and try to become a doctor instead.

To do medicine, I needed to get good A-level grades. So in the midst of crisis and upheaval at home, I set to work, studying long hours and doing everything I could to cram in that extra little bit of knowledge. I didn't have long to make a difference because the examinations would take place in just over a year, and I suspected a lot of things would happen in that time. Study was also a handy way to escape from all the other factors that I couldn't influence.

By good fortune, I passed my exams with the necessary grades to win a place at The Middlesex Hospital Medical School. When I arrived on that first day, I felt delighted, but at the same time I had a terrible feeling of guilt – the first of many to come – for being at college and having a good time while Chris lay at home. He was due to start at university when the accident happened. He had wanted to be a student, he had wanted to do all of the things that I was about to do, but his accident had robbed him of everything that I could enjoy. Going home to see him at weekends became harder and harder as the sense of guilt became more profound.

As the years passed, Chris became prone to common ailments, easily treated in a normal healthy human being but made far more complicated and dangerous for someone in his condition. He developed painful abscesses in his teeth. It was obvious they were going to require extensive dental work under general anaesthesia. This was going to be a major hurdle because his lungs had become weak from the many chest infections he had suffered and the respiratory centre in his brain stem had been damaged. This meant that the general anaesthesia would be particularly dangerous. What would happen to Chris? It was clear that what should have been a relatively minor procedure was going to be fraught with complications, any of which could kill him. Yet because of the pain, there was no alternative but to have the dental work done.

I was working as a registrar in anaesthesia at the Royal Free Hospital in London at the time, so I persuaded one of my consultants to give the anaesthetic and one of the dental surgeons to fix his teeth. Even though it was a dangerous task, they kindly agreed, and I knew that Chris would at least have the best possible people working on the case. So the operation went ahead.

After it was over, I waited for news. When it came, I learned that, despite all of their care and attention, Chris was in trouble. He hadn't come round from the anaesthetic. He wouldn't breathe on his own, and so had to be admitted to the Intensive Care Unit – the very unit where I was working.

I was relieved of my duties so that I didn't have the stress of having to treat my own brother, but seeing him there was a shattering experience. One moment I had been the doctor on the unit, keeping anxious relatives informed about their loved ones, and the next I too was a relative waiting for the doctors to tell me what was happening to Chris. It was a role reversal which made me realise again what it is like to sit in a waiting room outside an Intensive Care Unit, waiting for news, fearing the worst but hoping for the best. Slowly the long anxious hours turned into days.

Chris was in a critical condition for some time, but gradually he began to improve. As his strength returned, he slowly regained his ability to breathe, until he was ready to be weaned off the ventilator. Eventually he was well enough to leave the Unit and he made history as the first patient ever to be discharged from Intensive Care and go straight home.

With the pain of the abscesses gone, he was brighter than ever and enjoyed the prospect of being with my mother and father again. Everything returned to normal, life fitted into its previous routine, a strict regime based around Chris which for my family had become a price gladly paid. Once again, the years seemed to stretch ahead without change.

Then one evening Chris felt ill, so my mother put him to bed early. It wasn't an unusual event; like any of us, he was subject to minor infections and occasionally felt off colour, and so my mother paid little regard in this instance. Later that night, going to his room to make sure he was all right, she found him dead from an overwhelming chest infection.

Thirteen years of pain and struggle, of revelation and reward, were over. His death, though sad was at the same time a great relief, for him as well as for us. His was a shattered existence, but one which had had a profound effect upon me, leaving a lasting legacy.

It is still quite painful when I think about it, but living with Chris has given me an insider's view of what it is like – what it is really like – to have to face such a disability year after year after year, both for the patient and for their family and friends. It is very easy for doctors to tell relatives blithely that their loved one is disabled, or to see disabled people at outpatients, or perhaps visit them at their home, without ever realising the true impact of what has happened. The reality of caring for someone who is in that condition, how it affects the whole family, with a ripple effect spreading out to brothers and sisters and their husbands and wives, how it affects marital relationships, friends and social standing is often difficult to comprehend. It is an immense burden, and for some, too much to bear.

But it also gave me an insight into the hidden quality of life that can exist for someone with serious head injuries, provided enough resources are put into looking after them. How someone who is disabled should never simply be written off as a hopeless case, that there are ways for them to create a sort of new life – perhaps not one that you or I would choose but one with quality all the same – so that they can once again enjoy the world around them.

Perhaps the biggest lesson I learned is just how important it is never to crush the hopes of a relative in a thoughtlessly brutal fashion. It convinced me that there must be a better way of approaching these matters, and providing relatives with hope is perhaps the most vital thing of all. After all, if there really is no hope, what on earth is the point of medical treatment.

Relieved of their burden, my parents now seem as close as ever. They have resumed many of their old ways, and familiar habits. I believe their experience has given them an enhanced awareness and creativity in their later years. Few outsiders would believe that they have endured such trauma.

I sometimes see my brother's face in the faces of patients I have come across with similar head injuries. I recognise the little movements of the thumb or fingers which were his first signs of recovery, and think, too, of times we shared together as teenagers growing up. I still miss him.

Medicine has changed a lot since then, and I sometimes wonder whether the skills and knowledge that we have now could have saved him then? Perhaps if he had been ventilated immediately, and the oxygen supply to his brain improved, fewer nerve cells might have died, and maybe that would have made all the difference. Maybe that would have given him the reserve to have made a better recovery, so that he could have had a better life.

Then again, maybe it wouldn't have made the slightest difference.

Chapter Two

The Unit

IT ALWAYS COMES AS A SHOCK to see the person you love lying unconscious on a hospital bed, surrounded by monitors and medical machinery, and hearing the rasping breath of a ventilator blowing air into their lungs – a whoosh of air from a very expensive set of bellows causing the patient's chest to rise and then fall time after time after time. It's an eerily constant sound, as regular as a pendulum clock, the impersonal puff of a mechanical pump performing the act of breathing which the rest of us take for granted. Certainly, it's an accurate indication of just how ill our patients are, and how they rely on our help to keep them alive. But more than this, it is the characteristic sound of an Intensive Care Unit.

Above each patient's bed is a monitor, with several wavy lines of different colours constantly flickering across the screen. Each line records the measurements we need to see how the patient is progressing – arterial blood pressure, heart-rate, pressure inside the brain, and a whole host of others which may be tailored to a particular case. Figures at the bottom of the same screen will often record body temperature and oxygen level.

In addition, at the side of the bed, there may be a haemofiltration machine cleaning the patient's blood – a job left vacant by kidneys which are refusing to work. Blood flows from the patient's body through narrow, clear plastic tubes, into the machine and past a thin membrane where all the impurities are passed to a fluid on the other side. Electrically controlled drips and motor-driven syringe pumps also vie for space. Even the bed may be temperature controlled. It's a high-technology response to illness, providing us with a constant flow of information on the rapidly changing state of a critically ill patient. The health of every patient on this unit can change dramatically over the course of a single hour, and without these machines we wouldn't know what was going on. As in all battles, information is paramount. It allows us to alter our approach as new conditions arise, giving us at least the chance to ward off developments which could take that patient's life.

For those of us that work here, all of this medical equipment is familiar, but we never forget the impact it must have upon relatives visiting a loved-one for the first time.

Coming on to the Unit, it may be difficult to recognise even members of your own family. Patients' faces are distorted by tubes and tapes, and often swollen and bruised. It's an unpleasant surprise for relatives – the first of many upsetting jolts to come. Few people visiting patients on this unit come away without asking themselves how such a familiar figure – a mother, a father, a son or daughter, once full of fun and warmth, and laughter and life – could be changed so quickly to a mere outline of a person, robbed of all movement and expression, almost a husk of a human being. As the patient lies there, unconscious, and reduced to such an unresponsive state, kind words or a gentle caress – the common currency of love between two people – no longer bring any sign of reciprocation. It's as if all the bonds formed through the years have been broken, and only a terrible isolation exists. It can be a shattering experience.

Relatives respond with a mixture of horror and hope. They feel deeply distressed at the sudden transformation of someone they once knew. Sitting by that bedside, perhaps holding a hand that once held you, it is only natural to wonder if there will ever be such a thing as a normal life again? Yet an even stronger feeling, able to swamp all other thoughts, is the feeling of hope. Hope that there will be a happy ending to the horror story. Hope that this is only a temporary state, the start of an uncomfortable journey back to good health, a journey only made possible by modern intensive care. For many, that hope is justified.

More than three quarters of the critically ill people who come on to this unit will live, many against odds. Some, despite appearances, were never going to die, and all they needed was a few days of being looked after constantly, allowing them to make their own recovery. Some could have died, and without intensive care, would certainly have done so, but they pulled through because of the medical techniques, nursing skill and –

most important of all – the constant care which this unit can provide. And then there are some who should have died but continued to live despite being in a terrible state, and nobody quite knows why.

Overall, an Intensive Care Unit should be a place of optimism, even though the patients who come here are certainly all seriously ill. However, there is always the other side of the equation. I see little point in trying to disguise the fact that, for some of our patients, this unit will see their final days. If three quarters of our patients can expect to survive, it also means that a quarter of them are going to die.

At first sight, this may seem an extremely high mortality rate; it certainly far outstrips that of an average general hospital ward. However, the Intensive Care Unit has a very selective intake – the people we see are those who will certainly die if we do not admit them. Most of the people who come to us are so ill that they cannot breathe for themselves. Some have multiple system failure: their heart, kidneys, lungs and liver have all been damaged by disease. Others have multiple severe injuries from car crashes, falls or industrial accidents. Many have illness which would certainly have killed them just fifteen years ago, but they can now turn to recent medical advances for help. The surprise, therefore, is not that so many of our patients die but that so many of them do recover.

Despite the severity of their illnesses, the patients who are admitted to Intensive Care may be regarded as the lucky ones; at least they will have the best chance of recovery that medical technology and care can provide. Many other critically ill people throughout the country will never be given this chance because of the lack of resources allocated to Intensive Care.

The Queens Medical Centre in Nottingham is one of the largest hospitals in the country with over 1200 beds and about 80,000 patients admitted to the general wards every year. It is the regional centre for a wide variety of specialities such as neurosurgery, spinal surgery and vascular surgery – each with a heavy demand for intensive care. More than 160,000 people attended the Accident and Emergency department last year, some of them very seriously ill and about to die. There are only twelve adult Intensive Care beds in this hospital. Most continental hospitals of this size would have more than twice this number and spend five times the amount we do on intensive care.

It isn't difficult to see that with a large number of seriously ill patients, and a small number of Intensive Care Unit beds, we have no option but to operate some kind of selection procedure. That is why one vital condition separates patients admitted to this Intensive Care Unit from all of the other critically ill people in this hospital. After examining a candidate's medical history, and taking a lot of additional factors into account, we only admit patients who we think we could help to survive. No matter how harsh the decision may seem, there is no point in admitting a patient who is going to die no matter what we do.

We're not in the business of trying to postpone the inevitable. Some people, unfortunately, are too ill to benefit from Intensive Care, and trying to use medical technology to extend their days would be a cruel act, raising false hopes for their relatives and condemning them to an undignified and uncomfortable exit from this world. Our purpose is to prolong life, not death, and re-cognising hopeless cases is an essential part of the job. Everyone who comes to this unit must be thought to stand at least a reasonable chance of recovery. For many, it will be their last chance. But how do you decide who will benefit from Intensive Care and who will not?

It's a very important decision – probably the most important we ever have to make. In many cases it is deciding between the chance to live and certain death. Up and down the country, in Intensive Care Units just like ours, other doctors are having to ask themselves exactly the same question. The answer could one day affect you, your family or your friends. One day, it could also affect me. This is how I make up my mind.

In theory it is a simple decision. Medical training, and a know-ledge of how diseases progress and the severity of injuries which kill should enable me to make quite a good guess about who is going to survive and who is not, who I can help and who I can-not – which are the patients whose conditions are potentially reversible to a significant degree.

Most of the time these things do hold me in good stead, so that I can come to a definite conclusion fairly quickly. For in-stance, I know that there is no point in attempting to treat various forms of cancer, or people who have a long history of ever-increasing serious illness that has not responded to treat-ment. Unfortunately, they are going to die regardless of our best efforts. I have reluctantly learnt to accept this fact, but it doesn't come easy.

Reaching a conclusion based on theory is one thing. Standing by the side of a patient and actually deciding to let them die is another. Theory becomes flesh, and it is impossible to hide from the harsh consequences of refusing to treat that person against all the odds. But there isn't any hiding place: someone has to make this decision, and sometimes that someone is me.

It's a process which often begins with a telephone call. It may be a consultant from another ward, asking me to consider admitting a patient to Intensive Care. Although they describe the case, and tell me the reasons why they think a spell on the Unit might be suitable, the only real way to make a decision is to go to the ward and see the patient for myself. Knowing that this person is probably close to death, I go there as quickly as my commitments to other patients on the Unit will allow.

After I have introduced myself to the doctor and nursing staff on the ward, we discuss the case again and, if there is time, go through the records, examine the X-rays and review the patient's medical history, trying to identify the medical conditions that have brought them to such a perilous state. Often, however, the patient is so ill that action has to be taken there and then, buying us the time we need to reach a considered conclusion.

One of the basic steps of Intensive Care is to insert a tube called an endotracheal tube through a patient's mouth and into their wind pipe. This allows us to pump oxygen-rich air into their lungs, staving off death for a little bit longer. Usually, we can see the effects immediately. Blue lips and grey skin turn a healthy pink. A small plastic tube is placed into a vein in the arm and connected to a drip; an anaesthetic drug is injected through this cannula and the procedure is carried out while the patient is asleep. A plastic bag of fluid is squeezed gently into the bloodstream. Slowly the blood pressure begins to rise so that sedatives and painkillers can be given safely. The patient improves, and seems much more comfortable as the sedatives take effect. Easing a fellow human being's burden is one of the great joys of being a doctor. But taking this particular step is a double-edged sword; should I later decide that Intensive Care would contribute nothing to that patient's life, then I know I will also have to be prepared to withdraw the endotracheal tube and let nature takes its course.

On visits like these, I can see all too clearly the vast differences which exist between an Intensive Care Unit and a general hospital ward. Critically ill patients need constant attention, twenty-four hours a day. On the unit, there is one highly trained nurse for every patient and a specially skilled doctor is always present. On general wards, however, there may be one nurse between eight patients and the doctors may not be fully skilled in the practical procedures required to resuscitate a critically ill patient. Nor does the general ward have the equipment – the monitors, the measuring systems, the ventilators, and the plethora of infusion pumps and other machinery – vital in the fight to save a seriously ill patient's life. Looking after seriously ill people has become an entire speciality in itself.

The reason for the patient's deterioration is usually quite clear. Often they have had surgery, but have suffered a post-operative complication. For others, it is the just the latest, but the most severe, episode of a disease which has been getting progressively worse for some time.

We go through the case notes carefully, looking at what medical investigations have been performed, seeing the results of tests, getting as accurate a picture as possible of the patient's state of health, and all the time trying to work out the best course of action: what was the patient able to do at home before coming into hospital? Could they move around easily, walk to the shops and lead a normal life? Or were they restricted to a life spent between a bed and a chair, condemned to an existence in a nursing home without control over mind or bodily functions? In short I need to know what is the quality of life we are trying to save. Who looks after the patient at home; is there anyone who cares? What do they think? Has the patient ever expressed any opinion to help us decide what to do?

Some patients are not ill enough to merit admission to the Intensive Care Unit. Although poorly, they would improve under a tighter regimen of care and controlled treatment which could be provided either on the ward, or in a High Dependency Unit – a specialised unit which is able to offer a level of care that falls roughly halfway between that of an ordinary ward and an Intensive Care Unit. The decision is clear cut and easy to make with certainty.

Then there are those patients who I believe would benefit from Intensive Care. They may have a serious condition, but one that I know I can treat with a good chance of success. Once again, this decision is relatively easy to make, and I will admit them to the unit immediately. I know that they stand a good chance of recovery, and I also get pleasure from the feeling that I am doing all in my power to help them.

Next come the patients who I am certain are going to die no matter what I or anybody else attempt to do. Admitting them to Intensive Care would not prevent their death but would certainly stop them passing away with dignity. They would die unable to speak, attached to drips and monitors, robbed of individuality – and all for no good reason. We would be misusing our medical expertise in a worthless struggle against an inevitable outcome. Death would always be the winner, and in trying to prevent its arrival, we would have made that patient's passing harder still. In such circumstances, it is surely better not to intervene, even if this goes against the simple human desire to help. It's a difficult decision, but these days, I normally don't have many problems in making it.

My greatest source of concern lies elsewhere. These are the cases where I think that the patient is probably going to die – but I can't be certain. Uncertainty at any time can be an unsettling influence but when you are choosing between someone's life and their death it is a recipe for a very troubled mind. It's the grey area of medical decision-making which can best be summed up by the word 'perhaps'.

Perhaps if I give them a few days in Intensive Care, they could survive, though the odds are stacked against them. Perhaps I could try this technique or that, and perhaps it might make the little difference which often tilts the balance between life and death.

But there is another side to the argument. Perhaps by taking them into Intensive Care, I might be condemning them to a miserable existence for the sake of my own conscience. Perhaps what the patient needs most is not treatment, but courage from me to take an unpalatable decision and refuse to admit them. Perhaps by admitting them and filling a precious bed on the unit I will later have to refuse admission to another patient who might benefit more.

Research studies have produced formulas which allow you to enter all the factors of a patient's illness and come up with a figure that measures the severity of their illness giving a fairly accurate prediction of their chance of survival. For example, studies of one particular form of brain injury have shown that only 5 per cent of patients will recover – just five people out of every hundred.

Figures like these should make difficult decisions a lot easier, and they sometimes enter my mind as I walk towards a patient's bed to begin the examination that will decide whether they are admitted to Intensive Care or not. The trouble with them is that they don't tell me precisely who those five people are. Is it this patient, or that patient, or the one I saw yesterday, or perhaps the one I will see next week?

As I stand by the bed, the patient doesn't always know that I'm there. Whether the patient appears conscious or not, I tell them who I am, and explain what I am about to do. Even when they appear to be unconscious, you can never be certain just how much or how little such a patient can hear and understand, and I know that I would want to be treated with courtesy and respect if I was in their position. Many are utterly exhausted, overwhelmed by the thought that they may well die. Others simply lie there, too ill to speak, or may be beyond caring about one more person who has come to intrude upon what they would prefer to be private moments.

I tell them that I can see that they are getting very tired, and that I know they are having difficulty with their breathing. I tell them that I've come to see what I can do to help. In fact I usually say, 'I've come to see if we need to take you downstairs to Intensive Care, or whether there are a few things that we could do for you here on the ward.' I suppose it's playing with words when what I really mean is: 'I've come to see whether we should just simply call it a day and leave you in peace.' I do it to save the patient unnecessary anguish, but also for my own benefit. Words can be very effective bandages, and they can put a veil between yourself and the harsher aspects of life.

Some patients never realise the true intent of my visit, but others cotton on immediately, and there is no way of avoiding their knowing gaze. However, I never feel like a merchant of doom, attending at the critical hour. Instead, I always feel the patient's sense of relief. Critically ill people tend to know they are very ill, and their greatest fear is that none of the hospital staff will take their plight seriously. When I arrive, I'm regarded as a symbol that doctors are considering every possible option to improve their sometimes wretched condition.

Usually, I start by assessing their level of consciousness, then measure their blood pressure, listen to their chest, and look at the charts on the end of their bed which list the facts and figures that might reveal an overall trend. I'll also take a sample of blood from an artery in the wrist to measure how much oxygen and carbon dioxide is in the patient's bloodstream. This gives a good indication of how well the lungs are working, how much oxygen is getting to the brain, and therefore how well it is functioning. I'll also examine their intake fluid and urine output.

Behind all of these checks and tests and short conversations there is only one real purpose. All of the time, I'm searching for an indication that the illness this person is suffering from could be reversible. All of the time I'm trying to decide what to do.

Once the examination is over I discuss the case again with the doctors and nurses who have been looking after the patient, asking for their views, making sure there is nothing I have missed. This decision is too important to be confined solely to my own opinion. Maybe they will know something I don't or maybe have a different view of the case which might influence my decision or cast a different light upon my observations. I'll also discuss the case with the nurses who have been attending to that patient. They will know the patient best of all, having looked after them day after day, seeing any reason for sharp decline or, more importantly, any reason for hope. The nurses often give me a very balanced view, unclouded by a doctor's natural enthusiasm for treatment. You see, it is always easier to decide to treat than not to treat, to decide to do something rather than decide to do nothing, and doctors have been trained to think that they should always do everything in their power to save a life. Withdrawing treatment, deciding to sit on your hands and do nothing, can almost be seen as acquiescing with death.

And then comes decision time. There is no hiding place; the patient's relatives are sitting outside, and shortly I will have speak to them and tell them what we are going to do. After all the discussion, all the differing opinions, responsibility for the final decision comes down to me.

Sometimes, the details of the people I have seen in the past and the decisions I have had to make for them come back to me at the end of an evening. Years later, I still find myself wondering if I did the right thing. Sometimes I can even see their faces.

I don't have to try very hard to remember a young woman in her early thirties who had suddenly collapsed in her home and was rushed into hospital. She was admitted to an ordinary ward, but seemed to be making a full recovery as she chatted to her relieved husband and young children, all under six years old.

25

However, the scan revealed that she had suffered a brain haemorrhage. A main artery had burst inside her brain, depriving the tissue of oxygen, and although the bleeding had stopped temporarily, it would probably burst again, and this time she could die. The neurosurgeons decided that the only thing to do was an operation to clamp off the weakened part of the burst vessel, preventing the vessel from bursting again. It is a difficult and lengthy procedure, but since the alternative was almost certain death, they had no option. She would have to spend some time on Intensive Care after the operation as a matter of course to recover from the effects.

During such delicate surgery, which is performed under a microscope, a slight movement or misplacement of the clip is always a possibility. She was told about the inherent dangers of the procedure, but also the surgeons' hopes for success, and so, after discussing the matter with her husband, she agreed to surgery. He was with her as she was prepared for the operation, and would have had a last-minute chat before it was time to leave. The next time he saw his wife, she could neither speak nor breathe.

It doesn't matter how many times you are warned that a certain practice can be dangerous, few of us ever take it in. No one looking at the figures for the number of people who die in road accidents every year ever think that we will be the ones to die in a car crash. It will always be somebody else. But someone has to be on the wrong end of a statistical analysis.

This particular operation is an extremely difficult procedure – a life-saver when it works well, but the risks are high and it can also have catastrophic results. In this case, although the clip had been placed accurately across the burst blood vessel, its presence had provoked spasm in the blood vessels around it, shutting them off too. The effect was a serious reduction in the blood supply to neighbouring parts of the brain stem. As a result, her brain stem, the most important part of the brain which controls all of the essential functions of the body, was starved of oxygen. Within the space of just a few minutes, a substantial number of brain cells had died and the brain stem was now very badly damaged.

The surgeons were aware that the operation might not have gone well, but nobody could tell the full extent of the damage until the effects of the anaesthetic had worn off. When eventually she did regain consciousness, it soon became apparent that the only part of her body that she could move were her eyelids. She was perfectly aware of everything around her, but robbed of every other movement and facial expression. It's called the Locked In Syndrome: she was effectively locked into her own body, just like being locked in a cell where visitors can look in. She could hear what everyone was saying but was unable to say a single word in return, not even able to move her eyes. She could only communicate by blinking her eye lids, once for 'yes' and twice for 'no'. She was a free, conscious spirit, able to think clear thoughts, but unable to make her body move to give those thoughts expression. Although she could not have suffered any pain, it must have been an existence pretty close to Hell.

Some people have phobias about being buried alive. They have an unnatural fear of falling into a coma which is mistaken by doctors for death, and then imagine the terror of awaking to find themselves already inside a coffin and unable to get out. Here was the real-life medical equivalent.

What thoughts must have raced through that poor woman's mind as she came around from the anaesthetic and slowly, with ever increasing panic, began to realise her terrible predicament? At first she might have attributed her inability to move or speak to the effects of the anaesthetic, but then as her mind became more and more clear, she would have realised that something was wrong. Her first instinct would have been to try to tell a nurse or a doctor what was happening, but she wouldn't have been able to. She would have wondered if we were even aware of her predicament. All the time she would have been trying to comprehend what had happened, struggling desperately to work out what to do, unable to move a muscle to give vent to her feelings. All of the time, she would have wondered if she was going to remain this way for life? It's hard to imagine any greater horror.

Patients with neurological injuries may not move at first, but frequently there maybe a small improvement after the first few days. It is always difficult to assess in the early stages just how far this improvement will go. Not all of the brain cells may be dead. Deprived of oxygen, some may be in a state of temporary suspension, unable to work at the moment, but sure to recover with time. The only thing to do was simply to carry on with ventilation and wait to see what would happen.

Her husband, totally shocked, couldn't come to terms with what had happened. He had been devoted to her, and the love between them was obvious as I watched him hold her hand and tenderly stroke her hair.

Later, their two young children came on to the unit, to see their mother as she lay there, hooked up to a mechanical ventilator, and connected to monitors. Just the previous day, she had been sitting up in bed chatting to them. How must they have felt – unable to hear the sound of their mother's voice or feel the fundamental comfort of her embrace.

How terrible, too, that visit must have been for their mother, able to see her children and hear them speak, but unable to reach out and hold them, or even say or do anything to comfort their tears. It was utterly heartbreaking; so moving that, hard as I tried, I couldn't maintain the professional detachment vital to protect myself from the emotion of such occasions. Looking at that little group of people, huddled around the bedside, every member of the Intensive Care team could feel the tragedy seeping into our hearts however much we tried to resist it. I could see that the surgeon who had performed the operation was also deeply affected by the woman's plight. He had been trying to save her life by preventing a further serious haemorrhage, even though the risks were high. Somehow, the public expects doctors to lose all human emotions as soon as they put on a white coat. It had required a lot of courage to perform that operation knowing the terrible consequences should things not turn out as planned. I have a lot of respect for my surgical colleagues. They are expected to carry on treating other patients, often performing the same surgical procedure at the same time as having to cope with the painful knowledge of what has happened just hours before.

I spoke to the woman's husband the same day, and I explained that it was likely that she would die or at best be profoundly disabled. I went over the case again to make sure that he understood exactly what had happened, and what was the possible outcome. At the same time, I didn't want to destroy his hope, because hope is what keeps human beings going, and for all I knew at that time, she might recover to some acceptable degree. Although I could see the effect my words were having on him, his optimism that she would make a full recovery remained unshakeable. For the next two weeks, he sat at her bedside.

Sometimes, he brought their children with him and they would talk to her as she lay there.

Medical training teaches us to take the correct actions and make the right decision without having our thoughts distracted by unhelpful emotion. But from time to time we have come across cases which have found a chink in the armour and this was certainly one of them.

Leaning into her field of vision so that she could see us, we would look into her eyes and try to comfort her by telling her that we knew she could hear us and understand what we were saying. We explained to her what had happened and why she couldn't move. And we tried to give her hope, even though we felt that there was very little, because we knew that she would need hope to sustain her in the days ahead. She couldn't speak to us, but we could see changing expressions in her eyes, and almost read her thoughts there. Here was a personality, a character we could see and feel and speak to, but one that was still utterly beyond our reach.

As the days passed, she began to show signs of a slight recovery. After two weeks she been weaned off the ventilator and had been breathing on her own for forty-eight hours, and I wondered if this was a sign of things to come. Perhaps, after all, she would not die, but make sufficient progress to achieve some sort of quality of life. Years of torment for her and her family would lie ahead, but at least she would be with them, with the small chance of further progress still.

And that's when disaster struck. We had a bed crisis in the Intensive Care Unit. At that time we only had the resources to staff eight beds on our Unit and the demand for places was often higher than the number of available beds. Another desperately ill patient needed to be admitted, but there was no room.

Despite her serious condition, she was, compared with the rest of the patients, the healthiest person on the Unit. She could breathe on her own, which none of the rest could do, so if anyone had to be moved, she was the best candidate. I felt this was an outrageous state of affairs, and all of the team felt deeply unhappy. Although her breathing was strong enough to keep her alive without the support of a ventilator, she had no reserve which would enable her to combat any infection. Moving her off the Intensive Care Unit would certainly set her back, and would probably put her life at risk. In addition, she knew the staff

29

here. She needed familiar faces around her, people who she knew she could trust. She wasn't ready to go off the Unit – but we had to have a bed for another dangerously ill patient. Someone had to go.

She was moved to a general ward on the other side of the hospital – even though we knew that they couldn't provide the intensity of care she really needed. There weren't enough nurses to be able devote sufficient time to her. By necessity, she would be left alone for comparatively long periods. It was far from an ideal solution to the continual demand for Intensive Care beds but there was nothing else we could do. Unfortunately this is not an unusual decision to have to make, the same problem is faced by almost every Intensive Care Unit in the country. In hospitals from North to South, Intensive Care Units are often full and patients have to be moved out prematurely.

I didn't see her again for four days. That's when I received a call from the consultant on her unit, telling me she had contracted a chest infection, and asking me to consider once again admitting her to the Intensive Care Unit. A bed had now become available, so I went to the ward to carry out the usual pre-admission assessment.

When I saw her, she was already in a coma and any prospect she might have had of recovery was almost certainly gone. It was clear that the oxygen in her blood had fallen to levels so low that more damage to the brain had probably occurred. The secretions had built up in her lungs and as a result her frail breaths could not draw enough air into her lungs to provide an adequate flow of oxygen in the blood.

I could have predicted this would happen. Our worst fears had been realised. The only sure way to look after anyone in her condition is to keep them in Intensive Care. I wasn't really cross, but I was certainly upset, with mixed emotions. Technically, having got her on the road to breathing spontaneously, I would have liked to have given her a prolonged protected period to see if her breathing improved still further. That was what she would have wanted, and what I thought her husband and children deserved – a chance to recover. But circumstances had now changed significantly.

There was no doubt in my mind that her condition had become a lot worse since she left the Intensive Care Unit. In my opinion, it was extremely unlikely that she would make any kind of acceptable recovery now. Further brain damage had undoubtedly occurred, and I could see no benefit to be gained by taking her back into the Intensive Care Unit. Quite honestly, I felt that here was a chance to let her go, to release her from the torment and terror that she must have gone through in the past three weeks. Her passing would be a tragedy, but at least it would give her family the chance to recover with time. There is only one thing worse than a lingering death and that is a lingering life.

The senior nurse on the ward felt very strongly that the woman's husband had still not come to terms with the fact that she was going to die. He suggested that it might be kinder not to take the decision now, but to put the woman back on a ventilator simply to give the husband time to adapt to the situation. It was tempting to agree with him, and certainly this was the easiest option in the short term but I felt that if this was done, we would be stuck in an impossible situation. She would be on a ventilator for ever, stable but clearly not brain dead. At best she would be even more profoundly handicapped than before. Clearly, all hopes of recovery had been shattered by her move, and there was no point in pretending otherwise. After further discussion with the nurse and the consultants in charge of her care, we reached agreement on what to do. We would not admit her to the Intensive Care Unit. Instead, the chest infection would be allowed to take its course, and in the meantime she would be made comfortable and free from any pain or distress by administering whatever tranquillisers or sedatives were necessary. Now, it was time to speak to her husband.

We talked to him for over an hour in a small office next to the ward, explaining what had happened, and trying to make him understand that further treatment was pointless. He was still very optimistic abut his wife's condition, and we had to persuade him that his optimism was unfounded. I had to make him face the facts, albeit at his own pace, with a bit of gentle guidance and explanation. Slowly, the things that I was telling him began to sink in.

There were long periods of silence as I allowed him time to gather his emotions and ask any questions which would help him to understand. I told him that I had decided not take his wife back on to the Intensive Care Unit because I knew she was not going to improve. He asked me how I could be so sure. I explained how his wife's condition had deteriorated still further, and that even if I did take her back and cure her chest infection, it was only a matter of time before she contracted another one, and then another one, until the day came when an infection finally claimed her life.

As I spoke, I could see the pitiful sight of his confidence ebbing away, and when I had finished speaking, he sat quietly, with his head bowed. In the face of such evidence, he could no longer ignore the hard reality that his wife was slipping away, and that's when he cried. Soon, he would have to summon up the courage to tell his children that mummy would not be coming home. Tears welled up in our eyes too.

She died later that night. I knew she didn't have much reserve to fight off an infection, and I wasn't surprised that death had come so soon. Although I had become personally involved, something I try to avoid, I knew that this was the best possible ending to an impossible situation.

It was very important to me that we had taken the time to make sure her husband understood precisely what had happened, and why we had decided not to re-admit his wife to Intensive Care. He would have to live with this memory for the rest of his life. If we had left him with any unanswered question, any doubts that something more could have been done, they would have haunted him for years.

I wish I could say that we are able to devote as much attention to all of the relatives that I speak to in similar circumstances, allowing them as much of our time as they need to come to terms with the imminent loss of their loved one but often it isn't true. Even at times like these, we have other critically ill patients to attend to, and the conversations we hold are all too short.

Refusing to admit a patient to the Intensive Care Unit is a decision I have taken many times before, and many times since, but this case was different. Everyone on the Intensive Care Unit had worked so hard to get that woman to a point of possible recovery. We had come to know her, or know at least the person we thought she was, and understood the absolute fear which must have dominated her first few waking hours, and how as each day passed, it had been replaced by a brave acceptance. We had seen her husband's love for her and, knowing how he had kept his faith, we had wanted to do everything in our power to give her the greatest chance of life.

Logically, I knew that the decision not to re-admit her to the unit was the correct one, but emotionally, I always wondered if there was anything else I could have done. Given the chance, could she have improved still further, or would it have been a prescription for endless misery, for her and her family? If she had been conscious and I had looked into her eyes again, what would she have wanted me to do?

I thought about her for the rest of that afternoon, in the evening when I went home and even in the months that followed. Although years have passed since that time, I sometimes think of her still.

When deciding such important matters as who to admit to the Intensive Care Unit and who to refuse, it is tempting to distance yourself from the emotion of the occasion by lapsing into professional detachment. It is possible to view a patient purely as an unconscious physiological specimen; the figures generated by blood pressure measurements, heart-rate, urine output, X-rays and all the other medical methods of analysis can be viewed as cold data and interpreted using your medical knowledge, much as a car mechanic might tune an engine, or decide that the vehicle is beyond economic repair.

It allows you to view the patient dispassionately. A degree of detachment is absolutely essential to save the doctor from the colossal stress involved in taking such decisions day after day, and to avoid your own emotions colouring the decision-making process to the patient's disadvantage. However it is also important to take many other factors into consideration.

Sometimes, as a rule of thumb, I imagine that the person lying in the bed before me is my own mother, or father, or another member of my family. I try to think what would be the best thing for them if they were in this position. Would they want me to continue with treatment by admitting them to the Intensive Care Unit with all its rigours, or would they prefer to be allowed to die peacefully?

Every doctor will have a different approach, and a different judgement as to who is and who is not suitable to be admitted to the Intensive Care Unit. Some will err more on the side of caution, preferring to admit everyone they can, even when they know in their heart of hearts that the patient stands little chance of survival. Others will undoubtedly take a firmer line, refusing to admit unless the patient stands more than a borderline chance of survival.

In addition, the availability of beds on the Unit plays a part in the decision to admit or refuse to admit a patient. Sometimes there is, quite simply, no room at the inn. Under these circumstances, if we feel that the patient would benefit from Intensive Care we have several options, none of which is satisfactory. The first is to make room for them on our own unit by discharging another patient. This may be by prematurely discharging someone who can now breathe on their own and moving them to one of the general wards, or by transferring a patient to an Intensive Care Unit at a neighbouring hospital. A second option is to do your best to stabilise the new patient and then transfer them to another hospital where Intensive Care facilities are available. The third option is to open up an additional bed in the middle of the Unit.

All of these options cause delay and during this time the patient may deteriorate still further. Occasionally such decisions place a patient's life at risk. By the time I go to see the relatives, I have already made up my mind.

Any dithering must be confined to discussions with colleagues. You must have a positive approach, letting them know that you have thought long and hard about such an important issue before reaching a conclusion. They will need to have confidence in your ability to make decisions. Simply explaining the situation and then asking, 'What do you think?' won't do. You're foisting a decision that should be yours on to people who aren't in a position to take it.

If we have decided to admit the patient to Intensive Care, then we will also tell the patient's relatives the reasons why it is worthwhile continuing treatment. We tell them what the treatment will involve, and how it will affect the patient, so that they may prepare themselves for the sight of the person they love hooked up to a ventilator and surrounded by medical machinery. We also encourage them to have hope, but at the same time make quite clear – in cold stark terms if necessary – the possibility that their loved one may still die. It is vital to give them hope mixed with realism.

On the other hand, if the patient would not benefit from admission to the Intensive Care Unit, we explain carefully why further treatment would be pointless. The reason for this decision will be written down in the patient's notes.

I am always surprised by the calm acceptance that usually

greets such a disappointing opinion. Most relatives can see the deteriorating condition of the patient for themselves – sometimes even more clearly than we can – because they remember what that person was like in their days of good health. Some ask me to explain how I have reached my conclusion, but the most common concern is that their relative should not suffer any more pain, and they can see that prolonging treatment would have the opposite effect.

There are however, exceptions. I was once asked to see one elderly lady on one of the medical wards who had recently been admitted to the hospital with severe pneumonia. As she had been admitted as an emergency, little was known of her circumstances. However it transpired that she was living in a nursing home and suffered from dementia. Life for her had been pretty miserable for the last decade as the dementia had become progressively worse, robbing her of most of her mental abilities. Slowly, she had become more and more detached from the reality of this world, and lived in one of her own. She hadn't been able to lead an independent life for years, and there was no prospect of improvement.

We knew we stood a reasonably good chance of curing her pneumonia by admitting her to the Intensive Care Unit. Support for her breathing, and a stiff course of antibiotics would probably sort things out. However, there were other factors to consider. She was elderly, and frail, and probably didn't have much longer to live in any circumstances. We would be taking a frightened old lady who couldn't understand what was happening into a strange place and attaching her to machines. And when the treatment had succeeded how long would it be before her lungs deteriorated again? What sort of life would I be struggling to maintain – one of incontinence, and even further decline into eventual decrepitude.

Surely the pneumonia was nature's way of ending a pitiful existence. After considering we decided not to admit her to the Unit.

But when I came to explain this decision to the relatives I was shocked at their angry response. The old woman's son and daughter-in-law went beserk! 'Who are you to play God?' they shouted.

I listened to what they had to say, and considered their objections carefully. After all, these decisions cannot be taken lightly, and maybe they could provide another point of view which hadn't been considered.

As their anger and emotion began to subside, I detected the motivation for their unexpected stance which hadn't been apparent when the shouting began. It turned out that the son hadn't visited his mother at the nursing home for years. He had, for whatever reason, left the old woman to be looked after by nurses without ever taking time to see how she was. Now, as his mother lay dying from pneumonia, the son was wracked by remorse and was finding it difficult to cope with the thought that he had been guilty of such neglect. Maybe if he now protected his mother from such heartlessness, this would make amends in some way.

Here was the real reason for his objections. It was a sad story, and I understood how he felt, but our first responsibility is always towards my patient. We have a duty to do whatever is best for them, and it would have been quite wrong to subject this old woman to a terrible ordeal just to make her son feel better. My decision remained the same.

The son just would not accept this decision so I invited a consultant colleague to provide an independent second opinion. Sure enough, he too decided that it would not be appropriate to admit her mother into Intensive Care. After a further long discussion the son eventually concurred, but he still wasn't pleased. The old lady passed away peacefully the next day.

I had no doubt that her death was the kindest thing that could have happened. The ability to save a life which hangs in the balance isn't the only factor we have to consider when deciding who to treat and who to refuse. We must also look at the quality of life that person would have to endure should a stay in Intensive Care prove successful.

Sometimes, after deciding that a patient is a suitable candidate for Intensive Care, I will find someone who doesn't want to go there whatever I think. Often they are frightened of the prospect of being put on a ventilator and losing control over their lives, and in these circumstances, we can often persuade them that there is nothing to fear. They can then be admitted for treatment with their consent. Occasionally, however, we do come across a patient who feels that they have suffered enough and now want to be left alone to die. They have made up their minds long before I arrive to assess them, so that as I introduce myself and tell them the reason why I am there they simply say: 'Bugger off' or some other similar short expletive.

I often find it funny that patient self-determination in hospital, a subject which has inspired mountains of philosophical publications, can, in practice, be reduced to just two words. But the bluntness of those words is an indication of the certainty that the patient feels after long consideration of all the facts. Normally, I do everything that I can to respect this. We have no right to ignore another human being's wishes on how to conduct life and death. We are there as advisors not as dictators or moral guardians.

However, there are some occasions when we can't be certain that they really mean what they say. Low oxygen levels, common in very ill patients, make them extremely confused and agitated. It prevents their brain from functioning properly. It may be necessary to ignore the patient's apparent wishes under these circumstances.

Some time ago I was called to a ward to see one old man who was shouting and swearing and adamant that he wasn't going to go anywhere near Intensive Care. He wanted to be left alone to die, and when I turned up he told me to go away in no uncertain terms. We knew that we could help him recover. We tried to reason with him, but he was having none of it, and stuck to his guns. 'No, I do not want to go anywhere. Leave me alone.'

He had had an operation a few days before and now had a bad chest infection. Despite the oxygen he was receiving from a face mask, the level of the gas in his blood was still quite low. So I spoke to his relatives to see if he had ever discussed the matter with them. He had never expressed any particular wish on the subject. They thought that his outburst was entirely out of character and were sure that he would have given consent had he been rational. He had been playing golf the week before he came into hospital. Life hadn't been better since he retired five years ago.

This confirmed our suspicions. Ignoring his shouts we brought him down to Intensive Care, sedated him and put him on a ventilator to help his breathing.

Later, when he had made a good recovery, the man had no recollection of ever having objected to being brought down to the unit. Nor could he remember ever having seen me before on the ward, or telling me where to go, and what I could do with myself when I got there. Nor could he remember being moved from the ward to the Intensive Care Unit.

When I told him what had really happened, he didn't believe me. He had no reason to want to die, and felt terribly embarrassed. He just couldn't understand why he would say all of those things. But I could. The low oxygen levels, brought on by poor breathing, had made him very, very confused. He was, in effect, almost hallucinating. We had relied on our judgement to ignore his wishes, and it had been the right decision.

However, there is always the other side of the coin. I have come across patients who know exactly what they are doing, and who have made up their mind long before I see them, that life no longer has any further attraction. They want to die, and would appreciate it if we didn't try to interfere.

One such patient was a 45-year-old AIDS sufferer who had pneumonia and couldn't combat the infection effectively because of his impaired immune system. He was unconscious when I examined him, and it was obvious that the disease was fairly well advanced.

His father was a great strapping Yorkshire farmer, the sort of man who believed in calling a spade a spade, with definite views on homosexuality. It was clear that he had loved his son dearly throughout childhood, had been very proud of the boy, with great hopes for his future. Imagine the dismay when he suddenly realised that the apple of his eye was homosexual. It was a fact that the father had never been able to understand or come to terms with, and furious rows regularly split the household. After one particularly bad dispute, the two had gone their separate ways, unable to reconcile their differences. There had been no contact between father and son since that day.

Years passed. The next time the father saw his son, his boy, now a grown man, was lying unconscious on a hospital ward about to die. The police had contacted him as 'next of kin' and he had travelled through the night to be there. I remember wondering how intense his feelings must be as a father to have to face that situation – the feelings of guilt for all the things that had been said in anger in the past, for all those wasted years. The feeling that soon it might be too late to put things right. I had seen relatives with all of those feelings before. But in this case, there was another hurdle the father had to overcome.

Sitting beside him in the relatives' waiting room was his son's boyfriend, the man whom he blamed for luring his boy into a perverse way of life at a vulnerable age. This was the first time they had met, even though he had been his son's full-time live-in partner from the very first day he had left home. The father hated him, and although nothing was said, you could feel the tension, and almost hear his thoughts.

But after being by his bedside for some time, you could see things change. Whatever had happened in the past, it was now of no consequence. The only thing of importance was their boy, lying critically ill. Slowly, the farmer and his wife began to recognise the genuine love that this man had for their son. They could see that he was as devastated as they were, and as time passed a close bond formed between the three people, who had once been strangers and then enemies, but were now finally friends united by circumstance.

Although there was a reasonable chance that we could have successfully treated this first attack of pneumonia his boyfriend was adamant that his partner did not want to receive Intensive Care. They had discussed the issue many times, ever since he had first contracted AIDS, and he had left specific instructions that no attempts should be made to reverse any serious infection. He could see no point, knowing that treatment would simply be a postponement of the inevitable, leaving the way clear for yet more infections until death finally came. Instead, he should be allowed to die now, in peace.

Recognising their closeness, and knowing that any respite we could offer would be a temporary one, the father and mother agreed that this was the best thing to do. It was an incredibly brave decision. There was no doubt in my mind that what they were telling me accurately reflected the wishes the patient was unable to express. And so we respected their wishes, and apart from ensuring that the patient was sedated sufficiently to save him from pain, did not take any further steps to combat the infection which later claimed his life.

We were all touched deeply by this case, for I can remember still the sight of the mother, father and boyfriend standing with their arms around each other, heartbroken and crying, united in grief at the death of someone they had loved in different ways. And I remember thinking as I walked away, leaving them alone together in that small room, that this is what the milk of human kindness is all about.

Life would be very easy if we could predict with certainty who would recover and who would not. We would then know who to treat and who to let die, because in a strange way, my colleagues and I find it easier to cope with the fact that a patient we have struggled to save has died, then the thought that we have contributed to the survival of someone who is condemned to a life of misery and torment. Head injury patients in particular are extremely frustrating. Sometimes, patients who suffer only minor injuries become severely handicapped while those with severe head injuries make an unexpectedly good recovery. Statistically, we might be sure that ninety-five out of every hundred people with the same degree of severe injury will be handicapped or die, but we can't tell who is going to fall into the 5 per cent who will make a good recovery. This means that we have to treat every patient who comes before us with the assumption that they are going to fall into that five per cent, even though there is a 95 per cent chance of getting it wrong. This presents quite a dilemma as there is no room for half measures.

There are undoubtedly those who owe a continued full, active and happy life to the treatment they received in Intensive Care. They are the lucky ones. There are also those whose life we have saved, but who are now so profoundly handicapped that you have to wonder whether it might have been better if no attempt to save them had ever been made. Head injuries in particular are very difficult to predict because it is often only possible to be able to see the degree of true injury after forty-eight hours of treatment have elapsed, by which time a patient who some might consider would be better off dead is likely to survive.

There is no clear-cut answer, and the temptation for those of us in full health to judge what is or is not a life of sufficient quality is confounded by what some disabled people have told me after their stay on the unit. One recent case brought that point home to me very forcibly.

A young man – about thirty-five years old – had been in a car crash and fractured his neck. There had been substantial damage to the spinal cord, and he was paralysed from the neck down. It is impossible to either treat or nurse a patient with injuries like these without imagining what it must be like to have to face the consequences of those injuries yourself. I know that the prospect of being so disabled would fill me with horror, and most of us believe that we would prefer to die. The poor man was still unconscious and couldn't breathe for himself when he came in, but after several weeks he finally began to recover sufficiently to be weaned off the ventilator.

However, as time passed, he recovered still further, and eventually reached the point where he no longer needed intensive care, and despite his paralysis, could be looked after on a general ward. He did reasonably well for a week or two, but then, as is common in such cases, developed a very nasty chest infection. His weakened lungs were unable to get rid of the secretions, and this would probably be the first among many chest infections that he was going to have to endure. His consultant on the general ward called me up to see if I thought he was suitable to be re-admitted to Intensive Care, where I knew we could cure the infection. His was a bleak future, paralysed from the neck down, totally dependent upon nursing care for the rest of his life, with little or no chance of ever having a normal life again.

He was fully conscious when I came to examine him, and able to speak in a harsh whisper if someone put their finger over the tube in his windpipe. I was satisfied that he was rational and in full command of his faculties and well able to decide for himself what he wanted to do. I explained how, once he was put back on to a ventilator, it was very likely that he would have to remain on the ventilator for the rest of his days. Yes, eventually, he could have a ventilator installed in his own home, but once we had embarked upon this course of treatment, he might always have to depend upon a machine to take every breathe for him for the rest of his life.

He had no hesitation in agreeing. I asked him why he was so confident, and he explained that he had a wife and two young children. While he didn't relish the prospect of being paralysed for the rest of his life, he wanted to be able to see his children grow up, and he was prepared to live this existence for their sake. So we went ahead. He is now being rehabilitated in a specialist spinal injuries centre that treats patients who can't breathe. His home is being converted to take all the equipment required to care for such a profoundly handicapped person on a ventilator. A team of carers is being recruited to assist his wife. They will have to work in shifts, twenty-four hours a day, seven days a week. There is the prospect of an electronic pacemaker which can be implanted to stimulate the nerves that control his breathing but at best this will only free him from the ventilator for a few hours.

It was a fascinating conversation because it is unusual to be able to talk to someone in his condition. Normally, I would have had to make the decision for him, and I'm not sure that I would have come to the same conclusion. Some doctors, seeing a patient in his condition, would have taken the decision not to treat the chest infection, but instead let him die, under the impression that they were saving him from a life of unparalleled horror. But here he was saying that he wanted to live. It also made me realise the tremendous instinct for survival that we all possess. Even in the most appalling circumstances, life is a precious thing.

And yet will he feel the same way in five years time? Will his marriage survive? And what about the cost – not less than £100,000 a year for the rest of his life?

CHAPTER THREE

Dying with Dignity

EVEN THOUGH SHE WAS IN A SIDE WARD, everyone could hear her cries and sobs echoing across the Unit. 'He's not dead, I know he's not,' she said. 'He's going to come back to me. We have a young son, and I know he wouldn't leave us. I know he's going to come back to me.' For three hours she refused to leave him, beginning to scream as the body grew cold.

They had been together for over twenty years, and he was only in his late thirties when the brain haemorrhage struck. A blood vessel had burst without warning, cutting off the blood supply to the brain stem and starving it of oxygen. One minute he had been playing with his young son, and the next he had collapsed in a deep coma. For two weeks we had struggled to save his life but our efforts were in vain. A vital part of his brain was now dead, and nothing we could do would bring him back to life.

We had tried to tell his wife after the second set of tests showed that his brain stem was dead, but she wouldn't believe us. Instead she held his hand and cuddled him and told him that she loved him and simply said we were wrong. The ventilator had been switched off hours ago. There was no consent for organ donation. Hearing her sob was too much to bear, even for my consultant colleague, who has over twelve years experience behind him. He had to walk away, leaving only the nurse to witness her grief and comfort her.

When the chaplain arrived, I suppose she could no longer avoid the truth and that's when she began to wail uncontrollably, consumed by shock and unrelenting misery. Her father finally persuaded her to go. Speaking gently to her, he reached out his hand, helping her to her feet, put his arm around her shoulders, and slowly they walked away.

It's a story told by even hardened nurses on this unit, as proof that you never become immune to seeing the effects of death upon those who survive. Even now the memory can bring tears to their eyes. There is no easy way to face death, and in this unit, it is probably a more common sight than on any other ward in the hospital. When we realise that a patient is going to die, then it is up to us to look after them every bit as well as those patients who are going to survive, but perhaps in a different manner.

When asked to describe my job, I say that it is to provide patients with intensive care not intensive therapy. The two are not the same. There are times when to continue with intensive therapy runs contrary to the principle of caring for the patient. While the patient still has a chance of survival we must certainly employ all therapeutic methods at our disposal. There is nothing that we would not do if it could make even a slight difference between life and death for that patient. All of us on this unit have spent our professional lives trying to master techniques and skills which will bring critically ill patients back from the brink.

However, once we realise that we are not going to win, and that no matter what we do, the patient is going to die, then it is time to change our objectives. Instead of providing treatment designed to cure the patient – which has already been shown to be a worthless task – we must switch to a type of care which will make that patient's departure from this world as painless as possible. We must allow them to die with dignity.

Our prime duty to all of the patients in our care is not simply to keep them alive for as long as possible, but to produce survivors with some quality to their lives. We are not in the business of prolonging death. We have a duty to recognise when our patients want to die and ensure that their death is not a slow, painful, agonizing one in undignified circumstances. I certainly wouldn't want that to happen to me. One of the constant reassurances that I have to give relatives waiting anxiously outside the Intensive Care Unit is that their loved one is not going to suffer. Technically this form of treatment is known as palliative care, a course of action which has become well established in the field of cancer care. On this Unit we call it 'a good death'.

Recognising a patient who isn't going to make it isn't usually very difficult. They aren't responding to treatment and drugs to stimulate their heartbeat have to be given in ever greater doses. They need 100 per cent oxygen blown into their lungs by the ventilator and their kidneys have stopped working. Ever greater levels of medical intervention are required, and still the downward spiral cannot be halted. It's not a battle we give up lightly and occasionally it can be a very difficult judgement.

Nurses, who stay continually by the patient's bedside, are usually the first to notice the irreversible decline. They will know the patient much better than anyone else on the unit, and always feel it is their duty to prevent the patient suffering needlessly in the name of medical treatment. Inevitably, despite all of your best efforts, there comes a time when you have to ask yourself, 'Why are we doing this? What are we hoping to achieve?'

Some say these are questions we should never ask – that a doctor's duty is to use their medical skills to the best of their ability, to preserve life right up to the moment of death. In theory it sounds a good principle, and I suspect that it has been a useful tenet in the past. However, anyone who has seen the levels of intervention possible with modern medicine would be horrified to think of anyone they loved dying under such circumstances. Many of the techniques used, while invaluable, may be unpleasant and uncomfortable for the patient. There comes a time when the benefits of carrying out these procedures are far outweighed by their disadvantages. As in all things there is a line to be drawn where it is time to say, 'no more'. Exactly where that line should lie will vary from person to person.

Deciding matters of life and death, who to treat and who not to treat, is a very serious matter. It isn't something to be done lightly, without due consideration of every possible point of view and opinion. That is why on this Unit, we place an enormous amount of faith in a technique which has gained approval from Harvard Business School tutors and parish councillors alike. We hold a meeting or 'case conference'. These group discussions are easily the best method for finding a common way forward, drawing upon a wide range of expertise to give us the best chance of reaching the correct answer.

I suppose to an outsider, a group of people sitting in a room, perhaps drinking coffee and nibbling the occasional biscuit, may present a rather surreal approach to deciding who should be given a chance to live and who should be allowed to die, but nothing could be further from the truth. These meetings are always very carefully conducted, because a person's life will depend upon what is decided.

The group will usually consist of three doctors and at least two nurses. The doctors attending will be the Intensive Care consultant in charge of the Unit that day, and the Intensive Care consultant on call for the Unit for that week. The consultant who referred the patient to Intensive Care in the first place will also attend. The nurses present will certainly include the patient's own bedside nurse and the senior nurse in charge of the Unit for that particular shift. Combining such expertise gives a full medical picture of how that patient is likely to fare.

Nurses who have looked after the patient continually since they were admitted will probably have the greatest detailed knowledge of how the patient is progressing – or not. They are also most likely to be the people who question a doctor vigorously if they think that the patient's right to die a dignified and pain-free death is being ignored.

The nurses on this Intensive Care Unit are highly trained, dedicated people, who have a wealth of experience at looking after critically ill people, and they will certainly know more about the subject than many junior doctors. They also show an admirable trend to be rather assertive, and woe betide the doctor who cannot put up good reasons why treatment should continue despite a patient's inexorable decline. After all, the nurses are the people who will be expected to carry out the doctor's instructions. Everyone is free to give an opinion, from the most junior nurse to senior consultant, and no one's view is ignored or laughed out of court. Strangely, in all of my time in Intensive Care, I can honestly say that I have never heard a nurse argue that care should be continued when everyone else wanted it to stop. Usually it is the doctors who want to plough on against the odds, and the nurses who are demanding to know why.

Sometimes other people will attend these meetings for special reasons. Student doctors and nurses may be present so that they can learn how such difficult matters are resolved. Others come because they can offer information on the patient which might be relevant.

We review what treatment has been carried out so far, its objectives, and why it might not have worked. Our main aim at this stage is to come up with an alternative treatment strategy which might help the patient improve. All of the time we are searching for anything which we might have overlooked, a misinterpreted sign, a growing trend, a cause for hope.

The discussion is led by the Intensive Care consultant, but everyone has the chance to put in their halfpenny worth. Opinions will vary, and it is not uncommon for the referring consultant to be the least inclined to accept defeat and argue that the patient be given a little bit longer to see if an improvement in their condition is likely. The decision of the meeting always has to be unanimous – and unanimous without anyone's arm being twisted. Overall, the tenor is usually the traditional stance taken by all medical staff: where there is life, there is hope. No stone is left unturned, no technique or drugs which might help left unconsidered. If a person I loved was in this unit, I would want to know that the doctors and nurses here had done everything in their power to save that life, and so this is the principle I adopt for all of the patients in my care.

In situations where it is clear to everyone that we should carry on, or quite clear that we shouldn't, then the discussion takes place very quickly. In a situation where the overwhelming view is to discontinue, but a lone voice insists we carry on, that view is taken very seriously, and the issues raised discussed in detail.

Where we can't reach agreement, then treatment will continue, but often with a caveat that there must be a sign of improvement within an agreed time limit. Then we will review the situation and see if the original arguments still apply.

Outsiders may be shocked by what sounds like a school debating chamber deciding who should be allowed to die, but that image is deceptive. It is a very effective method of forming an accurate assessment of the true position and combining the knowledge and experience of the group's members. Each on its own could give a misleading view, reflecting whatever single discipline was dominant. It provides a forum where a multitude of different opinions can be considered and it is also far more reliable than allowing just one person, no matter how experienced to be the sole decision maker.

We are trying to act in the patient's best interests, using all the available information, but often this boils down merely to medical opinion. Relatives don't get involved, simply because they usually don't have the expertise to make an informed judgement. However, their point of view is still valued and strongly represented by the nurse looking after that patient, who will have made a point of finding out their views and will present them during our discussion. Often a family will tell nurses that they are certain that the patient would not want to suffer any more in the name of saving their life. If I am convinced that this is indeed an accurate and reliable view, then this would influence a finely balanced decision in favour of discontinuing treatment.

However, finding an accurate and reliable view from relatives is not always the easiest thing to do. As doctors we have a responsibility to do the best for the patient, and it is sometimes suggested that this equals doing what the relatives think should be done. In most cases the two are the same, but this rule doesn't necessarily always apply.

I remember an old chap who was about seventy-five years old and a bit of a boozer, who came on to the unit suffering from pneumonia. He was very ill, and couldn't breathe for himself. While waiting for a course of antibiotics to work, we had no option but to help his breathing by placing him on a ventilator, as well as infusing him with drugs to increase the beat of his heart.

From the social history in his case notes it was obvious that he was very well-off, a point backed up by his family when they came in to see him. However, later, they took me aside, and painted a picture of a stubborn old man, who drank himself senseless every day and was entirely dependent upon them. It wasn't the most charming image, and the impression I was left with was of an old man with a very poor quality of life, drinking himself into oblivion while waiting to die. Had he been a borderline case who looked like he wasn't going to recover, then such an image would probably have swayed my decision towards agreeing to withdraw treatment. I would have done it for the best possible motives, with the full support of his family.

The old chap did recover, however, and eventually left the unit. I assumed that he would probably return to his old habit of daily drinking, and could imagine a steady decline unto death, and I pitied his family who had to care for him. However, I was wrong.

He came back to see us three months later, and instead of a crumbling dependent pensioner, I was surprised to see an incredibly fit, very healthy and fiercely independent man. He was bright, articulate, and though he walking with the aid of a stick, I had no doubt that he wouldn't think twice about giving a bunch of thugs the hiding of their lives if the occasion demanded it.

I was struck by the disparity between the image painted by his relatives and the reality of this man returned to good health. I asked him to describe his health in the past, and he replied that he had always been independent – indeed he prided himself on it – and said that the day he needed to ask someone else for help was the day to give up. Hardly an accurate description of decrepitude.

Maybe he had been difficult in the past. Maybe his stubborn behaviour had made him into a burden, but even this couldn't account for his relatives' description which was so far from the truth. Instead, I found myself thinking uncharitable thoughts; I remembered his obvious signs of wealth, and wondered whether the prospect of getting their hands on a share of his money had influenced what they said to me. Perhaps they were tired of waiting, and the temptation to make their father's first stay in an Intensive Care Unit also his last proved too much. Anyway, from what I could see, they would have to wait a few years more before sitting down to hear his will read out.

Patients who come to Intensive Care cannot help but bring their personal lives too. Serious illness does not make time stand still, nor suddenly wash away the bitterness of years-old arguments which the patient may have had before coming to us. While most relatives regard a loved one's admission to Intensive Care as a time of crisis, for some it is a chance to settle old scores. And vengeance has no respect for a hospital bed.

Wives and ex-wives pose the most common problem. One of my colleagues remembers tending to a patient whom I shall call Mr Barker – not his real name. He had contracted a virulent bacterial infection after surgery into his abdomen, and now his body was beginning to react quite badly to the sudden invasion of hostile germs. Unable to breathe for himself, he was attached to a ventilator and, I must admit, to a layman, it would have looked a pretty bleak prospect. However, we knew that, with careful attention, Mr Barker had a good chance of recovering so when a nurse said that Mrs Barker wanted to talk to a doctor, my colleague intended to pass on this good news.

He barely had the chance to speak. Without further ado, Mrs Barker launched into a tirade, telling him how she strongly resented his attempts to keep her husband alive. She said that she and her husband had discussed many times what to do should he ever be in the situation that he was now in. He had made it quite clear, said Mrs Barker that he did not want to suffer what he regarded as the humiliation of a ventilator, and wished instead to be allowed to die in peace. In short, she wanted us to switch everything off and let him pass away. Her words weren't said as an expression of opinion. Instead, it was quite clear that she meant my colleague to take this as an order.

Now, he would have agreed with her if her husband was going to die anyway. Our job is to prolong life, not death, and we all firmly support death with dignity. But the fact of the matter was that her husband stood a very good chance of recovery. Yes, medical intervention was unpleasant, but dying, we suspected, was even worse. So he said as much to Mrs Barker, thinking that she would be pleased to hear this good news. He said: 'Your husband has a few years left in him yet, years that both of you can spend happily together.' But still she was adamant, insisting that nothing be done to save him.

Finally my colleague, a mild-mannered man, had to put his foot down. 'Listen, Mrs Barker,' he said. 'I respect your views, but my duty lies with my patient. We know we can save your husband's life, and we are going to do precisely that.'

Later on, after the nursing shift had changed my colleague was told that Mrs Barker wanted to see him again. Here we go, he thought, another ear-bashing about letting her husband die. So out he went, into the relatives' waiting room – and there stood a different woman. Embarrassed at bursting in he said: 'I'm sorry, I'm looking for Mrs Barker.' She replied: 'That's me.'

It turned out that this was indeed the patient's wife, or should I say his present wife. The first Mrs Barker was his ex-wife, who had never forgiven her husband for leaving her in the first place, and hadn't changed her name after the divorce. The present Mrs Barker certainly wanted us to do all that we could to save her husband, and seemed quite alarmed when my colleague mentioned that he had already seen the first Mrs Barker.

Perhaps the ex-wife really believed that withdrawing treatment was indeed the best thing for an ex-husband that she still cared for. Perhaps they really had discussed what he would like to be done if he ever found himself in an Intensive Care Unit hooked up to a ventilator. But we couldn't help suspecting that there were darker motives for wanting us to allow her ex-husband to die. Vengeance can be a long time coming, and crops up in the most unlikely of places.

Whatever the truth, Mr Barker didn't complain when he eventually recovered to lead a healthy life. However, we all sometimes wonder if he and his first wife still exchange Christmas cards.

Once the decision to withdraw treatment has been taken, it is our duty to speak to the patient's relatives to tell them what we have decided and why we have come to that conclusion. We have a policy of utmost honesty on this Unit; relatives are kept fully informed of a patient's progress and if we think a patient may survive, then we tell the relatives exactly how much hope there is. However, this also means that when a patient's prospects are bleak we try to prepare them for the worst, so news of our decision seldom comes as a surprise. I never look forward to these meetings, but there is no alternative, so together with the nurse and with a heavy heart, I join the family huddled in the small relative's waiting room and flick the sign on the outside of the door to 'engaged'.

Their reaction is usually one of relief, because they can see for themselves that the patient has not been responding to treatment, and perhaps the most common complaint at this stage is that we didn't reach the decision sooner. No one likes the sight of a mother or father lying unconscious on a hospital bed, hooked up to a plethora of machinery. It goes against every image of death with dignity, and there is always a sense of unease and concerns gently expressed: 'Doctor, is this really necessary. When the answer is no, then we have a duty to say so.

But there have also been situations where a family has vigorously rejected our opinion and demanded that we do everything possible to keep that patient alive, regardless of the indignity and distress it may involve.

I remember one family who found it impossible to accept that their sixteen-year-old daughter was dying from kidney, heart, lung and liver failure. We had fought hard to save her life, but she was slipping away before our eyes and further treatment would certainly have meant carrying out further uncomfortable procedures for no good cause. Her father couldn't believe that this could be happening to him, and when I told him that we had decided not to prolong his daughter's misery, he was distraught.

'How can you be so sure she won't recover?' he pleaded. My heart went out to him; if I had been in his position, I too would have wanted to clasp at any straw, any hope that my little girl still had the chance to live. I explained the diagnosis again, pointing out all the signs that death was imminent regardless of what we did, and hoped that he would understand. But it was no good. He wasn't yet ready to accept that he was just about to lose his first-born child.

I offered to have one of my colleagues come along and give an independent second opinion, but that wasn't good enough either. We were tainted by working for the same unit, and the father didn't trust our independence. Some doctors might have drawn the line at this stage, and simply gone about withdrawing treatment regardless of her father's wishes. However, I am always aware that a relative will never learn to cope with the death of a loved one unless they know that everything was done to save that life. Niggling doubts which begin 'What if . . .' have a corrosive effect on the mind as a person lays awake at night, pondering the tragedy and wondering why it happened. The only way around this is to answer every possible question as fully as possible.

I asked him to nominate a doctor of his choice, and he suggested his own General Practitioner, who had been a friend of the family for years. We agreed that this should be arranged urgently. In the meantime, the little girl remained on the ventilator, her life supported entirely by machines, until the GP came along. He was a kindly, hesitant man who admitted that he had never been inside an Intensive Care Unit in his life. Ignoring the mass of data available on the monitoring screen he felt her pulse and listened briefly to her chest, just as he must have done on countless occasions when she had suffered the usual childhood illnesses. He knew nothing of Intensive Care but he knew about people.

There was no hope and the GP knew it. He agreed that further treatment was useless. After speaking to the family privately he re-emerged and passed on their consent to withdraw treatment. Slowly the ventilator was turned down, and as her heart weakened the young girl who had been the subject of such dispute was allowed to pass away.

I did not resent in the slightest the GP's opinion being sought. Relatives have to live with the bereavement of a loved one for the rest of their lives, and his was an opinion they could respect. If that is what they wanted then how could we stand in their way?

Although I have never had an argument with relatives over the right to withdraw treatment, should that day ever arise, then position in law is quite clear. If the patient cannot give consent themselves, then it is the doctor, not the relatives, who must act in a way which is considered best for that patient. If a doctor in an Intensive Care Unit feels that continuing treatment is not going to benefit that patient, and the patient is going to die anyway, the doctor has the right to act accordingly. It is to be hoped that no doctor will ever reach the situation of having to use such a heavy-handed approach. Since it is such a sensitive and important issue, we prefer to reach agreement by discussion, and the way this is conducted will have an effect upon the relatives which may last for years. A moment's insensitivity or a sense of undue haste caused by other urgent matters will quickly be forgotten by the doctor, but will be remembered by the relatives.

The actual mechanism of withdrawing treatment is quite simple. The ventilator which has been pumping large volumes of oxygen-rich air into the patient's lungs is adjusted so that it produces a flow of air equivalent to a normal breath and the oxygen concentration is reduced to 2 per cent – that of ordinary air. Drugs which may have been administered to stimulate the heart or subdue infection are withdrawn. When these supportive measures are withdrawn, some patients die very quickly, sometimes within minutes. That is when I realise just how powerful Intensive Care treatment can be and also how heavily that patient has relied upon artificial support for every breath they take.

The only drugs administered are those aimed at reducing either physical or mental pain. We use mainly morphine or diamorphine – commonly called heroin – given in such doses as to ensure not just the patient's physical comfort but their mental ease as well. They are very soothing drugs, well able to combat pain, and the patient relaxes within minutes of receiving them. Our only objective is to relieve suffering. Usually the patient is deeply unconscious and they cannot communicate any last wishes, it's probably better that way. I usually tell the relatives: 'They are in a dream-like state, very like the sort of light sleep you have just before you wake up in the morning. They are aware of what is being said and comfortable but unable to respond.'

We encourage the relatives to speak to the patient, even though it may appear that they are asleep, or too ill to reply. At the end of every life there are always loose ends, and there must be an opportunity for the relatives to say things which perhaps they will have wanted to say for years. In many ways, this is more important for the relatives than the patient. They will have to go on living with the thought of unfinished business, and sometimes this can be a heavy burden to bear.

Seeing someone who is suffering intolerable pain is a very uncomfortable experience. Standing by the bedside and hearing their uncontrollable moans and cries as the agony surges through their body, it is inevitable that you will want to do all in your power to help them. I can see why some doctors can be tempted to stray across the line which separates justified treatment from illegal killing in extreme cases, where a patient they have known is in unbearable agony and crying out in pain. I suppose the closest the average person in the street will have come to this emotion is during childbirth. Seeing their wives suffering as labour progresses, husbands may lose control as they realise there is nothing they can do to prevent the person they love from going through this agony. I've known some to shout at and even attack a doctor or a midwife in a misdirected attempt to make things better.

Doctors suffer similar emotions, but for them the dilemma is much worse, because they know that they do have the power to turn off pain – all it takes is a single injection. Although it is illegal to administer any drug with the primary intention to end a life, it is standard practice in these circumstances to give dying patients a large dose of sleep-inducing, painkilling drugs to ensure they do not experience either physical or mental discomfort. We do this, despite the knowledge that in some cases however carefully judged the dose might be, this action might bring a patient's end a little closer due to the secondary effects on their breathing and their heart. We remain on the right side of the law, only because our prime motive is to relieve suffering and not to kill the patient. There is a fine legal line which separates a merciful death from a mercy killing. However, it is a line we are careful to ensure we do not cross.

Euthanasia is a term which is often used loosely, and as such means different things to different people. It comes from two Greek words: 'eu' meaning good, and 'thenatos' meaning death – a good death. Surely it is the duty of everyone looking after dying people to ensure just that? A good death; death with dignity free from physical and mental pain.

This is the true meaning of euthanasia but in practice it can be applied to a wide variety of circumstances. Withdrawing intensive care in itself could be said to be a passive form of euthanasia. When a patient is entirely dependent on fluids and drugs to support their blood pressure and heart beat, you know that patient is not going to survive very long if you withdraw that treatment, and so it could be said that you have killed them if you take this step. If you do this after it has been decided that the patient will not survive anyway, despite all of the best care that modern medicine can provide, then surely it is the disease that has killed the patient and not the doctors.

A good death is perfectly legal in this country and, in my view, there is nothing wrong with using heavy doses of sedatives to relieve pain and suffering, even though as a secondary effect, the patient may die more quickly than they might have had you not administered the drug. This is the acceptable face of terminal care.

However, administering drugs which could have no purpose other than to kill the patient is clearly murder, and quite rightly so. There have been successful prosecutions in the past against doctors in this country who have administered such drugs to patients dying in great pain, because it was felt that the chosen drug could do little to alleviate their mental or physical suffering or provide any other benefit apart from killing them. Ironically, had those same doctors administered a heavy dose of a strong painkiller, which would almost certainly have hastened their death as a secondary effect, they would have had a cast-iron defence because it might be reasonably assumed that the drug was prescribed with the primary intention of relieving suffering.

Most doctors who specialise in Intensive Care are also fully trained in anaesthesia and as such are skilled in the use of drugs for pain relief. It is standard practice in our Unit, and in Intensive Care Units across the country to administer large doses of such drugs to dying patients to ensure their comfort. In some cases this may significantly hasten the patient's death.

I don't see anything wrong with this, and I'm sure most people would accept that, as trained specialists, we are acting in an area where we have sufficient knowledge and expertise to be able to make an accurate judgement of what size of dose was necessary for that particular patient.

Given the choice, which would you prefer? Would you choose

to end your final days on this earth in pain and mental anguish? Or would you wish for the soothing effects of morphine, a powerful pain killer and sedative and probably the kindest drug known to man. I know which choice I would make.

I was only about twenty-four years old when I first used morphine to save a patient from a painful death. I remember her well. She was an old lady with a strong personality and a very sharp mind. Although well into her seventies, she was very articulate and in control of her faculties and she and I got along very well. Once, she showed me some photographs, and I remember being surprised, because they showed her as an attractive young dancer who looked roughly the same age as me instead of the old woman I saw before me now. It made me realise that we are all going to be old some day, and here was someone who, despite appearances now, had probably lived the same sort of life that I was leading, and felt the same sort of emotions that I had felt. Someone who, but for the passage of time had been just like me or one of my friends.

I was one of the resident junior doctors in the hospital, and I talked to her quite often. She had no family or friends, but now, after years of living alone, she was suffering from cancer and it had spread to other sites in her body including the spine. It had softened the bones in the vertebral column and some of these had become crushed by the weight of her own body. She could no longer sit or stand but was condemned to lie in bed for the rest of her days. In effect, her back was broken in several places. The cancer was out of control, beyond the point of X-ray or drug treatment. Every time she moved, the broken bones grated against each other. She was in excruciating pain, despite the regular high doses of pain killers that were prescribed. Whenever I had a quiet moment, I would talk to her. I could see her eyes light up as she remembered those far off carefree days of youth. I enjoyed her stories and it was clear that her pain would ease a little as her mind was distracted from the thought that she would have to be turned again soon to save her from suffering the additional discomfort of pressure sores.

One night, she could bear it no longer and nor could the young nurses who were expected to carry out this torture as part of their nursing routine. I was summoned to inject her with morphine directly into her vein. I could see how much she was suffering, and welcomed the relief given to her by the drug as much as she did. The effect was dramatic: one minute she was convulsed with pain, the next she was relaxed, as if a tense spring had been removed from her body.

The following day, she called me across and said quite bluntly, 'I know I am dying. What will it be like at the end?' She explained that the previous night's pain had been almost unendurable and she couldn't stand the thought of going through such agony again. I explained that it was not necessary because we could always give her intravenous morphine to give her relief from such an ordeal. Eventually she said: 'I want you to make me a promise. I want you to promise me that, when the time comes, you will give me enough morphine to put me out of my pain.'

Looking into her eyes, I could see that she had thought about this matter long and hard, and had clearly made up her mind what she wanted done. I understood that she meant that I should give her sufficient morphine to relieve her pain, even if she might not recover from such a dose. I told her plainly that there would come a time when the dose required to relieve her pain would be so large that it might depress her breathing. She assured me that it was not death she feared the most but the pain. I agreed to do my best to ensure she died in comfort. It was an easy promise to make, but not an easy one to keep. As days went past, she would call me over and say, 'Don't forget your promise now will you?'

Then one night the staff nurse rang to say that the old lady was in severe pain and was asking for me. I went to her bedside, and I could see that she was relieved to see me. Although nothing was said, we both understood that she wanted to escape the agony. The nurses had already given full doses of the pain killers that had been prescribed, but clearly she needed more; only a doctor could inject the drug directly into her bloodstream. So the night sister and I drew up a large dose of morphine to inject into her vein as I had done before to keep the pain under control. She saw us preparing the injection, and I told her that I was going to make her comfortable and that there was nothing to worry about. Then I pushed the needle into the tube leading from the fluid drip into her arm and gently administered the drug. I needed to inject much more than I had ever given before. Each time I would give a little more and then wait for some effect. Eventually, I could see her pain subside, and gently she drifted off to sleep. After hours of agony, with no respite in sight, she was finally able to rest. Later that night, she died.

It made a lasting impression on me because I had crossed the line between therapeutic medicine and palliative care for the first time. Up until then I had only ever administered drugs with the sole intention of making someone better. But now, even though my primary aim had been to ease a patient's pain. There was little doubt that the drug had shortened her life. Had I helped her to die? I felt I was in territory I had never journeyed through before. However, she had died with dignity, in the manner of her own choosing, and knowing this, I didn't feel any guilt. This is what she had wanted and I felt that I had kept my promise.

Since then, I've come to realise that it is accepted medical practice for terminally ill patients. We have recently conducted a survey into the people who have died on this Intensive Care Unit over the past year. In more than 85 per cent of cases, the patient died after we had decided to withdraw treatment and sedate them to keep them comfortable. In other words they were planned 'good deaths'. In many of these cases it is possible that the drugs administered might have hastened their passing.

We looked to see if any of the five Intensive Care consultants – myself included – was doing it any more than the others. I'm relieved to say that we had each taken these decisions with approximately the same frequency. Was it possible that we could be accepting defeat in some cases where, if only we had persevered a little longer the patient might have survived? Using sophisticated statistical techniques to test this hypothesis, we found that the death rate on our unit was no different than expected, when adjusted for the severity of initial illness. We take this as evidence that our judgement is generally correct. It is proof enough that the patients who have died on this Unit would have died whatever we had done.

However, we are working in a very dangerous grey area which is wide open to legal challenge. Knowing this, the important thing to do is to document everything very carefully, to show that your prime motive when prescribing a drug is pain relief. Each dose which is administered must be recorded carefully in the notes, together with the reason why the drug was given, and the thoughts which prompted such a conclusion.

Although the procedure I have described is accepted practice in every Intensive Care Unit in the country, as far as I am aware, there has never been a formal legal ruling on the matter. I'm sure it is best that this area of medical judgement should be left vague so that the individual circumstances may dictate what is best done, not a judge and jury sitting in a distant court room, none of whom have had practical experience of such situations.

It is essential that such decisions are made by a group – not one individual – and that they are reached unanimously. There are sometimes occasions when the lone voice urging continued treatment is right and the rest of us are proved to be wrong. One such occasion comes to mind. The patient was a man in his mid thirties who, after minor surgery, contracted a bug which attacked his muscle tissue. It spread rapidly throughout his body, turning his flesh gangrenous, and without radical surgery to cut away the infected parts there was no doubt that this man was going to die. The first episode of surgery did not halt the infection, so he went back to theatre for yet more of his flesh to be cut away. But that didn't work either, so still more surgery was required. Finally, we had reached a quite horrific stage, where almost half of the patient's upper body and abdomen had been cut away. Huge areas of his body wall had been removed, as well as most of his bowel. Looking at this poor man, it was difficult for even the hardened professionals on the Intensive Care Unit to believe that he could ever survive. Many of us felt that the surgical mutilation was going beyond the limits of what was acceptable to do to a fellow human being. Even if he did survive, what sort of life would he have? He developed a chest infection which deteriorated despite high doses of antibiotics. His kidneys began to fail. Every day he had to endure the discomfort of having dressings packed deep into his wounds. The nurses on the unit felt strongly that the time had come to say, 'Enough is enough,' and I agreed with this view.

We held a meeting to discuss our medical objectives in this case, and this opinion was strongly expressed by everyone – except the surgeon who was performing the radical treatment. All of the Intensive Care Unit staff felt that we should call a halt and allow the patient to die. However, the surgeon remained cheerfully optimistic that he could save the man's life. No, he couldn't give us any indication of what his chances of survival were, but he had heard of cases like this where the patient had recovered. He wasn't sure if those success stories had been in such a severe condition as his patient. Nevertheless, he felt confident that, with the assistance of plastic surgery, the patient's wounds could be made to heal. Yes, he conceded that the man may require artificial feeding for the rest of his days, but argued that it was still worth continuing the treatment.

Since no decision to withdraw care is ever taken until we have a unanimous opinion, a good old British compromise was reached. We reluctantly decided to carry on – but with an important caveat. We would continue for another forty-eight hours and if by that time there was no sign of improvement, we would definitely pull out. In addition to the patient's plight, I felt great sympathy for the nurses who were obliged to carry out unpleasant instructions without the comfort of believing that they were doing the right thing.

Much to our surprise, however, the man, or what was left of him, slowly began to recover, and in time left the Unit alive to tell the tale. I saw him by chance several months later and was amazed to see what had been accomplished by reconstructive surgery. He was eating normal meals and was clearly delighted to be alive. It was a case where a surgeon's very aggressive treatment had been justified. The surgeon had been right, and we were wrong.

The biggest problem we all face when making difficult decisions is, how do you know when you've put a patient through enough pain and anguish in the hope that they will get better? It's a bit like climbing Everest: if you don't try very hard, making repeated attempts if necessary, then you won't get anywhere. I remember one lady in her mid seventies who was admitted to hospital with a ruptured aortic aneurism – the main artery coming from her heart had burst. It's a serious condition which kills many people, but in her case surgeons had been able to sew a special plastic tube in place of the damaged vessel sealing the hole. It's a delicate surgical procedure, but one akin to patching a hole in a bicycle tyre.

She was admitted to the Intensive Care Unit as a matter of course to recover from the operation, and at first she seemed to be making good progress and was quickly weaned from the ventilator. But then she picked up a chest infection, and began to deteriorate. A course of antibiotics slowed down the infection, but not quickly enough, and within days, her kidneys stopped working. We side stepped that problem by placing her on a haemo-filtration unit to artificially clean her blood. But her condition deteriorated still further, and as her ability to breathe fell away we were left with no option but to put her back on the ventilator. She needed more and more drugs to keep her blood pressure at normal levels, and slowly but surely we were being drawn towards the extremes of medical intervention.

Her family were very distressed by the sight of their mother unable to breathe for herself, her blood flowing out of her body to be filtered and then flowing back in again, and all the drips and motor driven syringes that were vital to keep her alive. It wasn't what they wanted for a woman in her seventies and I began to wonder myself if it was the right thing to do. Would I want to see my own mother in such a condition? She had been on the ventilator for the past three weeks of treatment and little had changed. Again the questions began to surface in my mind, did we stand any chance of bringing this poor old woman back to good health or were we just prolonging her death?

After considering all of the circumstances, I felt that she should now be allowed to die with dignity, and could see little purpose in pursuing a fruitless cause at her expense. However, the surgeon who had performed the graft across her aorta felt strongly that it was right to continue. He had invested a lot of his time and effort into this lady, and he wasn't prepared to give up. I remember the discussion becoming quite heated. Surely he was just expecting us to treat his own inability to come to terms with failure? The surgeon stuck to his guns. He argued that she had lived a very active life, had been in full control of her faculties before the blood vessel burst, and that there was no reason to believe that she did not have the reserve to pull through. So we decided to continue a little longer.

More days passed. The ventilator continued to blow air into her lungs, her blood still flowed out of her body through clear plastic tubes, through the filtering machine and back and still there was no sign of improvement. Her relatives were becoming very agitated. They could see no point and no end to the treatment. They knew the surgeon was sticking out for a recovery and asked me what I thought. In matters like these we feel ourselves bound to support whatever decision the meeting to discuss her case had reached. It's akin to accepting Cabinet Responsibility which is the convention where politicians publicly support decisions reached in Cabinet even though they may privately disagree. So, swallowing hard, I told them that it was too early to give up, and yes, there was still a slight hope that she would recover. If she did, there was no reason to suppose that she wouldn't continue to lead the active life she had before her illness.

They had begun to pick up the difference in views on how their mother should be treated before asking my opinion, so that my words, although loyal to the cause, didn't carry much weight. I found it very difficult talking to them because I knew that my heart just wasn't in what I was saying. I could see that old lady suffering as much as they could, and yet I had to abide by the party line. It is one of the few times that I haven't been completely honest with relatives, and I felt extremely uncomfortable.

Finally we held another meeting to review the situation. The surgeon still felt very strongly that she should be given as long as necessary to make the recovery that he felt sure was just around the corner. But this time others felt equally strongly that he was wrong and I remember the discussion ranging over some interesting ground before we finally reached another compromise. Again it was agreed that she should be given another forty-eight hours' intensive care, after which we would need to see some signs of improvement to justify keeping her alive.

I suppose you could say that we had struck a deal more than reached a decision. Some could compare it to horse traders haggling for an advantage, or perhaps politicians thrashing out a collective view on a contentious issue. But whatever the analogy, I believed that we had finally reached the right decision, and the next forty-eight hours would see any argument resolved. The meeting had set two important criteria which would have to be met before it could be said that the old woman had improved. The amount of oxygen carried in her blood would have to rise, and there should be no evidence that she required greater levels of drugs than she was already receiving to support her heart. For an elderly woman in such a condition it was asking a lot and I felt sure that it was now just a matter of time before we would be stopping treatment and allowing her to die in peace.

I didn't hold out much hope, but two days later when I went to her bedside I could see I was wrong. There had been an improvement, and what's more, it looked like it might continue. So we carried on. And she continued to improve, slowly at first, but then with a quickening pace. Soon she was off the ventilator, and then the haemo-filtration machine, and she went on to make a complete recovery. Her family was delighted. Like me, they had given up all hope of ever seeing her back on her feet again. And, I must confess, had the decision been left to me alone, they never would. I had wanted to let her die but here she was, alert and very much alive. My colleagues and I had been wrong. Perhaps this was the exception which proved the rule. Maybe ninety-nine times out of one hundred other old ladies in a similar position would have died, so justifying our strong stance against continuing treatment.

Years have passed since this case, but unfortunately there have been few other similar success stories like it. The fact remains that she had been on the unit for over eight weeks – that's over fifty-six days at a cost of about £2,000 a day to the National Health Service, a total of £112,000. Many would argue that it is an inefficient use of tax payer's money to spend that amount on one woman in her mid-seventies, who in all probability will die within a few years anyway. I can see their point, but they have the luxury of absolute detachment and we have the disadvantage of standing by the patient's bedside where we can see a person rather than a statistic.

If that old woman had been their mother, would they hold a different view?

CHAPTER FOUR

Relatives

THE SCUFFLE HAD BEGUN in the relatives' waiting room, then spilled out into the corridor, and I knew it wouldn't be long before the two of them came to blows. On and on it went, the shouting and swearing, each of them threatening to beat the living daylights out of the other and, much though I tried to ignore it, finally I had to go out to see what on earth was going on.

There they were, facing each other like alley cats, the wife and the ex-wife, ready to do battle over the man lying critically ill just yards from where we stood. Summoning up my most soothing tone of voice, I appealed to them both to keep quiet or, if they couldn't, then to settle their differences elsewhere because they were disrupting the Unit and frightening the other relatives in the room.

For a while it had no effect, but slowly the two began to see sense, and gradually the argument settled down. They were still furious, but at least they were speaking to each other in semi-civilised tones, so I turned to walk away, secretly pleased that my diplomatic skills had worked wonders again. And that's when the patient's girlfriend turned up.

He didn't look the type, but then, who does? In his mid-thirties, reasonably fit, a striped-shirt-and-suit sort of person, he could have been a salesman for all I knew. But there was certainly no doubting his popularity – or perhaps I should say his former popularity, because there wasn't much of it left in the relatives' waiting room that day.

Off they went again, the three of them this time, shouting and screaming and hurling insults, each of them threatening to put the other two into intensive care alongside the man they each

64

thought should be theirs alone. He had been involved in a car crash, and thanks to the mercies of sedation was sleeping blissfully through the whole thing, totally unaware that he was the cause of a blazing row which showed no signs of abating.

What could we do? We tried appealing to their better natures, but it was no good. On and on they went, each of them shocked by this unexpected development, which was now blurring what had previously been clear battle lines. It wasn't a happy occasion.

'I'm going in to see him,' yelled one. 'Over my dead body,' yelled the other. When the dust finally settled, the true story emerged. The man and his ex-wife had divorced because of his affair with the woman who was now his wife. It had been an acrimonious parting, and the ex-wife had never forgiven the new wife for luring her man away. For years the two had avoided seeing each other, but the car crash put paid to all that. Neither of them had known anything about the girlfriend; she had been the patient's little secret, and would probably have remained so had not cruel circumstance intervened. And now, here she was, standing in the same room as her lover's wife and ex-wife in a scene straight out of a Brian Rix farce. Actually, I felt very sorry for her, because it must have taken a lot of courage to come to the Intensive Care Unit, knowing that it would bring her affair out into the open. All three must, in their own way, have loved that man dearly.

In the meantime, the quarrel presented us with a practical problem: which one of them were we to regard as the patient's next of kin? Usually, it is a man's wife, but in this case which one? After all, he had been married to his first wife for quite a long time, so she surely had a right to know what was happening to him. His present wife certainly had a strong claim, as his legal spouse. But his girlfriend had also been with him for a long time – albeit in a less-formal capacity, and she too had a right to know what was happening to the man she so obviously loved.

When a patient has a large number of relatives, the common practice is to nominate one person who can then relay developments to the rest of the family and friends, thus reducing the number of visitors who come to the Unit. But in this case, we couldn't depend on any one woman to tell the other two what was going on.

Unsure of what to do, we asked ourselves what the patient would have wanted us to do had he been conscious and able to speak. Others would have come to a different decision, but we felt that we had no right to ask any of the three women not to visit the man. There was no doubt in our minds that he would have wanted to see all three – but perhaps not at the same time. So we called them together, and told them what we were going to do. Each would have a fixed visiting time, far enough apart from the other two to make any more unplanned meetings impossible.

No one was ecstatically happy with this suggestion at first, and for a while it looked like World War Three was going to break out all over again. But they eventually agreed, because behind all the arguing and shouting lay one unpalatable fact. Nextdoor, on the Intensive Care Unit, lay a man who was critically ill, and they had all come to see him and all hoped he would get better.

And that's what happened, every day for the next five days until the man was well enough to leave the Unit and go back to a general ward. First the ex-wife arrived, stayed by his bedside, spoke to him, and murmured how she loved him before leaving again. Then came his wife, once again sitting by his bedside, holding his hand before she too had to leave. And finally his girl-friend arrived, and did the same thing. And throughout the entire five days, the man knew nothing about it.

Sometimes, I wonder what he must have thought, as he regained consciousness later to learn that his affair had been revealed in such a public manner. I also wonder what the three women must have said to him when he was well enough to listen. Each would have been afraid to say anything at first in case he died, but I suspect that immunity would have vanished when it was obvious he was well on the road to recovery. From then on, I suspect that any wishes for his continued good health may have been said through gritted teeth. It's probably the one time that a temporary relapse would have come in handy.

Apart from the odd horror story, however, my dealings with relatives in general have been warm and friendly. They are one of the pleasures of our work because we don't usually have any emotional contact with the patients themselves. Most of the people who are admitted to this unit are so ill that they are either unconscious or need to be heavily sedated for the entire duration of their stay. When they are well enough to regain consciousness, or have no further need for sedation, then they are well enough to leave Intensive Care, and may safely be moved to another ward. It is one of the frustrations of Intensive Care that we seldom get to know our patients in the same way that doctors and nurses on other wards take for granted. It's like doing a job but seldom having the satisfaction of seeing the fruits of your labours. Instead, everyone here gets to know the patient's relatives, and through them we get to know the patient by proxy. It is another one of the unique relationships which separates Intensive Care from most of the other departments in this hospital.

Relatives provide a vital link between us and our patients. We depend upon them to arm us with a character description of the unconscious figure lying on the Intensive Care Unit bed. It's the one bulwark against the temptation to regard that sleeping figure as a collection of medical data in human form. Here on Intensive Care, the drugs which free our patients from pain also put them to sleep, robbing them of their usual mannerisms. Even their face is often distorted by a tube blowing air from a ventilator into their lungs, and so we have no map with which to plot their identity. Only when we are deprived of hearing someone speak, or watching the changing expression on their face do we realise just how much all us rely on such gestures to mould our impression of a person. The light in their eyes, the tone and warmth of their voice, the way they move their hands to illustrate their language, all of these things tell us what that person is like. The only information we have on the Unit comes from the relatives and so we ask them to show us what that person is like, through their eyes.

Listening to what they have to say, we use the snippets of information to construct our own impression of that patient. Hearing the general description of how they have lived, and adding our own imagined details of mundane everyday life to that sleeping body, we can grant it a character of our own making. It's like listening to a radio play, and seeing the images of each character flickering across your mind's eye.

Often, my image is far removed from the truth – such distance is revealed only when I finally get to see and hear a patient speak for themselves and the gap between my impression and reality is usually enormous – but it doesn't matter. The picture painted by friends and relations plays a vital role in reminding us that it is a person we are treating, and not just a head, or a heart or a lung. They tell us what the patient is really like, and bring in photographs of them in former days. Often the smiling faces I see in

these pictures bear little resemblance to the swollen face, sometimes battered and swathed in bandages, that is the only other
image I have. The people in those small colour photographs
often seem like people from another world. Few of us ever
photograph sad times, and so the pictures I see have always been
taken on sunny days with blue skies. And there is the person I
am treating, joking and laughing with friends, or being hugged
by their children, playing on a beach, a moment of happiness
seemingly without end. Wives often bring in photographs taken
at their wedding, and show me their husband standing by their
side, dressed in a suit and looking slightly self-conscious. Yet
here, lying on the bed is the same man in different circumstances,
and sometimes, though I try very hard, I can barely recognise the
similarity.

It brings home to us that every patient here has had another
existence free from monitors and a machine to take their every
breathe, and seeing that other life makes us more determined that
they should have the chance to live that way again. But it also
enhances the pain for us when they die.

I find that elderly people want to tell me all about their early
life, and what they did when they were young. Old women
whose husbands have been admitted to Intensive Care often want
to tell me how they met, and how dashing he looked, young and
strong, and how he went off to war, but lived to tell the tale. It's
as if they are really trying to say: 'You may think he was only a
milkman, and therefore not important in your eyes. But let me
tell you that he has been a man of note in his time.'

Old men will tell me about their wives, and how beautiful
they looked when they first met, and how they wed, had children, and stayed together through the years. 'Times were hard,
but we worked together,' they will say. And I suppose that must
be true because I am always struck by the look of utter loneli-
ness, bewilderment and desolation on their faces in the moments
after their partner has died. Often I have seen old people, in the
aftermath, leaving the unit, knowing that they would be going
home to an empty house for the first time in over fifty years. I
can imagine them putting the key into the lock, opening the
front door and then closing it behind them, the sound swallowed
up by a silence so strong that you could almost reach out and
touch it.

When the relatives of our patients come to this Unit, they are invariably under a huge amount of stress. There is no escaping the harsh fact that the person they have come to see is seriously ill, and often at the point of death. Uncertainty is the worst pressure they have to deal with. Not knowing whether the patient is going to live or die is far worse than being told that all hope has gone and the patient is going to die. At least death is a certain outcome and it is possible to prepare yourself for even very painful events. But not knowing what is going to happen, to hope, and then to have all hope shattered, only for those hopes to rise again, is a particularly devastating form of physical and mental torture.

Some might say that on Intensive Care it is the patient who has the easiest time. Potent drugs used to sedate them relieve most if not all physical discomfort and so they spend their time on this Unit peacefully asleep. The relatives waiting by their side have no such luxury. Seeing the strain on their faces, and in some cases watching their physical decline, I have no doubt that, were I their family doctor I would regard them as patients too, in desperate need of counselling and perhaps tranquillisers to ease their anguish.

Outside this Unit is a waiting room, with soft, almost comfortable chairs, where relatives can sit down and have a cup of coffee. It's not the most inspiring place to have to face such an ordeal, but it's the best we can offer. Many of the people who wait here are too much on edge to relax in any circumstances, and would be satisfied with any room as long as it contained that one vital commodity – a payphone. Other people are waiting to hear news, and it is probably one of the most heavily used telephones in the hospital. We also have rooms where they can stay overnight, but only for a short period. There is a bed and a settee which can be converted into another bunk, where those waiting night after night can get some rest. This hospital is a regional centre for many illnesses, and patients are referred to us from all over the country. Relatives sometimes have long distances to travel, and it is easier for them to stay here, where at least they have the comfort of knowing they can be contacted quickly should a patient shows signs of deterioration.

It is common for relatives to be afraid to leave the unit; it's as if their mere presence is a protecting influence, a talisman which can ward off illness like an evil spirit. They feel, too, that going home to get some sleep is somehow letting their loved one down, shirking their duty, or quite literally, sleeping on the job. Since they feel their loved one is suffering – which often they are not – relatives feel they should suffer too, and running themselves to a point of exhaustion is a small price to pay for keeping loyal guard. Some illnesses are mercifully short, and the patient quickly gets better and moves off the Intensive Care Unit, bringing the relatives' vigil to an end. Other illnesses are also short, but this time the patient doesn't recover, so that death also brings the vigil to an end. But then there are the others.

Some patients have to stay on the Unit for weeks, and this has a devastating effect on the relatives. I see them outside in that small waiting room, worried, wondering, exhausted yet still living each day minute by minute, and this goes on for week after week. Every aspect of their life is thrown into chaos. They take time off work, send the children to other relatives and cancel all engagements to wait anxiously outside this Unit. The ordeal is made worse by the fact that many Intensive Care patients are in an unstable condition, so their prospects of survival can change very rapidly. One minute they may appear to be getting better, and the next they seem to be in a relentless decline. These fluctuations place the relatives on a roller coaster of emotion. They experience emotional highs and lows which are often out of all proportion to the patient's overall illness. An expert in psychological warfare could not have devised a more effective tactic, and after a while, the strain becomes too much to bear.

At the same time, with each passing day, the practicalities of life begin to impinge, bringing more pressure to bear on an already tense predicament. There is a limit to how much time anyone can take off work, and how much time anyone can spent away from home and the rest of the family. Some relatives go far beyond these limits, but not without paying a heavy price. Slowly, with passing time, they realise that they have no option but to go back to work, to look after the family and to spend more time away from the unit despite the patient's illness. And that's when the guilt sets in.

In addition to worrying about the patient, relatives are often worried about themselves. On the one hand they may be thankful that the patient has at least survived the terrible injuries inflicted by illness or accident, yet worry about how are they going to cope when it is time to take them home. How are they going to manage with a wife or husband who is severely disabled? How are they going to live their own lives yet care for someone they love? And when things are looking bleak, relatives often find themselves wondering, 'How am I going to cope on my own when they die?'

They feel very guilty because they are thinking about themselves when they feel they should be thinking only about the patient. Many find it hard to come to terms with their thoughts; they aren't the sort of things they feel they can talk about openly for fear of being branded selfish. Yet I can understand their worries, and they seem very natural to me. Often strong bonds develop between the relatives of different patients and this allows them to share their common feelings.

Most of the relatives I meet are warm, friendly people, even though the circumstance of our meeting is far from ideal. Normally, we don't get much hostility or conflict between the staff and the families, but sometimes, people can react to death in peculiar ways and I occasionally encounter a family who thinks that we could have done more. They find the death of their mother or father or brother or sister impossible to come to terms with – especially if it is a sudden death – and therefore yield to the temptation to look for someone to blame. Sometimes they blame me.

Struggling to save a life, trying everything you can thing of, anything which might make a difference as time ticks quickly away, is a frustrating and exhausting experience. Walking away from a bedside knowing that all of your efforts have failed and the patient has just died, can leave all of us feeling low. It doesn't matter how many times it happens, or how many different cases we see, often we find ourselves going through the scene again in our minds, wondering if there was anything else we could have done.

Once we can do no more for a patient and death has occurred, we have a duty to look after the relatives and, unfortunately, this sometimes involves being the target of suspicion. Grief takes many forms, and most relatives behave with great dignity under pressure, there are many who become irrational. The accusations which flow may be unpleasant, but they still need to be answered with care and patience. Only by satisfying questions and doubts will relatives ever achieve a state of mind needed to begin the task of coming to terms with their loss. Since my colleagues and I are the only ones who have the authority to provide a satisfactory explanation as to why the patient could not have been saved, we simply have to understand their feelings and take time. It isn't easy, and there are some people we will never be able to convince, but that doesn't mean we shouldn't try.

Sitting in the small waiting room can sometimes feel like sitting in the dock. Family members who think they have a grievance will take it in turns to accuse us of not trying our hardest, or not doing the right thing, or not really caring whether the patient lived or died. Sometimes, they will use a tape recorder, or one person will take down the entire conversation in shorthand, and you know that every word you say could be used in evidence against you. It's an unnerving feeling knowing that one poorly chosen phrase, one inappropriate word spoken in a moment of tiredness could form the basis of a court case. The questions come thick and fast: why did you do this, why didn't you do that, and surely you could have done much better? The message behind the questioning may never be openly declared as relatives struggle to conceal their anger, but often, as tempers flare, someone will come right out and say it: 'This person would still be alive if you had done your job properly.'

It's a painful accusation at any time, but coming so soon after we have done our best to save that life makes it even worse. Having to endure the helplessness of seeing a human being die despite all our best efforts, and then being blamed for that death just minutes later, can be very hard to take. Thankfully, I have a reasonably calm nature, and so I never lose my temper in these circumstances.

After listening to their questions, I usually react in two ways. The first thing I think is: 'Are they right? Could we have done more?' If something has gone wrong, I am usually one of the first people to know it. Even if I am satisfied that every procedure was correctly followed, every decision taken was the best one given all the facts available at that time, I will still listen patiently to what the relatives have to say. They may well have seen or know something that I don't, and so it is always worthwhile considering their views. Afterall, they have just suffered a bereavement, so giving them time to make a point is the least I can do.

If something has gone wrong, then we have a policy of honesty in these matters. This may not be something that many lawyers would like to hear, but in my experience, relatives usually understand that you have tried your best to save that patient's life, even if a medical accident has occurred, as long as you are honest. It's only if you try to hide the truth that you run into problems. They will invariably find out that something is amiss, and resent being misled, as would I under the same circumstances. Fortunately, medical accidents don't happen very often, so I have seldom been in this predicament.

I would like to think that every patient who comes to this unit receives only our best efforts to keep them alive. No one who works in this Unit does an intentionally second-rate job when someone's life is at stake. But as in all things human, standards sometimes slip or circumstances occur that are beyond our control and the patient suffers. When this happens, I will tell the relatives exactly what has happened and why.

Having heard their views, however, a more common conclusion is that everything that could have been done was done, and painful though the fact may be, the death of that patient was unavoidable. I wish it were otherwise. I wish we had the medical skills to save the lives of all of the people who come on to this Unit. But it just isn't so. A quarter of all the patients who come to Intensive Care will die, and however much we try, there is nothing that we can do to stop it.

Most relatives do automatically accept that we are doing the best thing for the patient, even though on this Unit we may have to do some very unpleasant things to their nearest and dearest. Supporting a patient's breathing by placing them onto a ventilator – and most patients in this unit need ventilation – is just one example. The procedure involves passing a tube into their mouth, down their throat and into their windpipe, so that a puff of air enriched with oxygen may be delivered without much effort from them. It is done to overcome what may be a temporary drop in the efficiency of their lungs – a weakness would prove fatal without our intervention – but it is nasty, although an anaesthetic drug is given to cover this manoeuvre and the patient sedated to minimise discomfort.

There is one side-effect which few people realise when we first tell them that we are going to connect them to the breathing machine. The tube blocks the vocal cords, as well as obstructing the mouth, and since the flow of air is controlled by the machine rather than the lungs, speech is impossible until it is removed.

To those who are healthy and fit, a temporary loss of speech may not seem like an insuperable disadvantage – nor is it for those of our patients who do improve and recover sufficiently to come off the ventilator again. For them, the silence was a price worth paying, a small disadvantage to a treatment which tided them over their worst moments until they were better. However, there is another category of patient for whom the words spoken immediately before the tube is inserted will be the last they will ever say on this earth. They are the people who do not recover, but under continuing treatment, spend their final days in an enforced silence before lapsing into irreversible unconsciousness and eventual death.

We know there may be things that a patient will want to say before the tube is inserted so, where possible, we summon the relatives to their bedside for a few minutes beforehand. These are vital words. Just think of how much we associate the person we love with their voice. It's as easily recognised as their face, and the prospect of never hearing it again is often difficult to bear. It's like dying by degrees, and relatives who fear that a loved one may not recover often take this silence as an ominous omen for the future. Unfortunately, giving the patient and relatives time for a last conversation is probably more an exception than a rule. Usually, we will have no choice in the matter. The patient may arrive on the Unit from theatre already on a ventilator, or else the deterioration of their breathing may be so rapid that action must be taken to save their life before relatives arrive.

Seeing the person you love undergo such unpleasant treatment, it is sometimes easy to forget that it is being done in a good cause. Doctors who carry out these procedures hundreds of times every year will often take the unpleasant side-effects that the patient experiences for granted. The effect upon a layman, however, can be devastating and without good communication, I can't blame them for becoming upset.

One day, one of my colleagues admitted a woman suffering from abdominal sepsis – a very serious infection which, left untreated, would almost certainly kill her. Quick action is vital in such cases, so surrounded by nurses, he set to work, treating the woman as best he could – and that's when her husband arrived, brandishing a very heavy torque wrench, and said: 'Which of you bastards is trying to kill my wife?'

He had come to the Unit straight from the scrap metal yard where he worked, and looking at him standing there, wearing an oil-soaked overall, you could see that he had spent quite a few years bashing the hell out of cars, probably with that very wrench he was holding. He was very big, and extremely aggressive, and it must have been an interesting experience trying to save someone's life while being in fear of your own.

The infection, which had started in her gallbladder, was now spreading into the bloodstream and she was going downhill rapidly. She had been complaining of pains in her tummy for the previous two weeks, but her doctor hadn't realised what was wrong with her. The poor woman hadn't been treated very well nor had her complaints been taken seriously. By the time someone realised just how ill she was, her health had deteriorated to the point where she needed emergency treatment. And now here she was, seriously ill in Intensive Care with what should have been an easily preventable condition.

Frustrated by how other doctors had ignored his wife's earlier complaints, her husband had greeted news of her admission to Intensive Care as yet another blunder, done purely for our own amusement. Grabbing a wrench, he had jumped into his car and raced off to the hospital, determined to 'sort us out'.

Looking at him standing there, my colleague had no doubt that this wasn't an idle threat. He could see that this was a man who had probably 'sorted out' quite a few people in his time, and as the nurses edged away towards the top of the bed, it was obvious that an explanation could not be postponed to a more suitable time.

'Look, we're not trying to kill your wife,' he said, 'We're trying desperately hard to make her better. Go and sit down in that chair over there and you can watch what we are doing.'

Unfortunately, at that moment, he was sticking a scalpel into her neck and was preparing to insert a large plastic tube into the jugular vein. There was blood all over the white bed sheets which was not the most obvious evidence that his wife was in safe hands. Nevertheless, the man sat down, and watched, and waited.

Slowly, he began to calm down. The tight grip on his wrench weakened, and after a few minutes he put it down. Instead, he buried his head in his hands, and then sat back with worried expression, relieved but still very nervous about what was happening. Seeing that the worst was over – or at least hoping it was – my colleague seized his chance. 'There's nothing you can do here but get in our way,' he said, 'Why don't you go and get yourself a cup of tea, and I'll have a chat to you later?'

And that's all that he needed. The big man, stood up and left, taking his wrench with him. Later, he apologised for what he had done. Relieved of the pressure, he was actually a very nice man who simply didn't know how to cope with his wife's serious illness. He was frightened by being in a situation where he had absolutely no control, and didn't understand that what looked like painful procedures were necessary to save his wife's life. In any case, they were being carried out under local anaesthesia. The decision to let him sit and watch – even though he hadn't had much alternative – had made him part of the medical process for the first time in the whole episode. At last he felt that someone was taking the trouble to explain what was going on.

He was an intelligent man, and quickly understood for himself what we were trying to do. After his wife was on the road to recovery, he returned to the unit to say thank you. We understood precisely how he felt. The feeling that he had absolutely no control over what looked like brutal things being done by doctors to his wife had frightened him and driven him beyond reason.

On this Unit, we have a policy of keeping relatives fully informed of everything that we intend to do, and the reasons why we are going to do it. Apart from treating the patient and relatives in the same way as we would expect to be treated, it defuses many potential sources of shock. Walking into an Intensive Care Unit, and seeing their loved one lying unconscious on a bed surrounded by monitors and machinery can be a terrifying experience for relatives. With some of our more severe cases, it can look for all the world as if the patient has absentmindedly fallen asleep in the middle of a NASA control room. Who can blame the relatives if they react in what might not be an appropriate manner?

That fear of being out of control, of becoming a number as soon as you are admitted to hospital, with no say over what happens to you or your family, is a very real one. It is the most common reason why relatives and patients react angrily to medical staff. Having all independence taken away from you is a horrible feeling, but there is no doubt that this feeling of helplessness hits hardest those patients and relatives who are a little bit brighter than most, or who are used to making their own decisions in every aspect of their life: patients who have been professional people, or who have run their own businesses, who have become used to making up their own minds on what they want to do, from the moment they wake up to the moment they go to sleep. Naturally, they resent surrendering any control over their lives, and this also extends to how their relative's illness is treated. They dislike a doctor simply telling them what is going to happen, but expect to be told the reasoning behind any course of action so that they can make up their own minds about whether that is the right thing to do. Since most of our patients are unconscious, we encounter this approach most often from the relatives. However, unlike some areas of the health service, we welcome their enquiries. It gives us the chance to discuss the case, and hear relatives' views on the efficacy and ethics of treatment which can sometimes rest against the outer limits of medical intervention. Listening to their opinions makes us re-examine medical decisions taken earlier to see if they withstand scrutiny in a new light.

In stark contrast, other relatives seem willing to accept every word a doctor says without quibble. They are used to being told what to do and what to think every day of their lives: what time to report to work, what to do when they get there, what time to have lunch, what time to finish, and thanks to television, what time to go to bed at night. They aren't used to making decisions, and view the whole medical process as one of the facts of life, seldom making a fuss.

There isn't much privacy on the Intensive Care Unit. The beds are positioned next to each other, only a few feet apart, and the most you can do is draw the curtains around the bed area to shield the patient from view but this does nothing to make every word of an intimate conversation less audible. The nurses try to provide as much privacy to relatives as the care of their patient will allow, and will often withdraw discreetly while continuing to observe the vital signs on a monitor at a neighbouring bed. Despite this there are frequently occasions when we are unintentional witnesses to everything a family may want to say. It isn't an ideal arrangement, but one forced upon us by necessity. However, although there is little we can do about it, we often feel that there are some conversations which no one else should have the right to hear.

Nurses on this Unit are frequently privy to the most moving scenes as relatives express feelings of intimacy, guilt, rage or just plain sorrow. They are the sort of conversations we have all had in our most private moments, each word driven forth by intense emotion, and the knowledge that this may be the last chance ever to tell that person your true thoughts, some of which may have been harboured for decades. Secret desires, wishes, actions, bitterness or love stored up across the years of a lifetime. Words of utmost tenderness, scenes of anger and recrimination, acts of forgiveness – the heights and depths of human feeling murmured to a sleeping patient in the cold, clinical setting of an Intensive Care Unit. Always, there is a sense of urgency. Often, time is running out.

No one would choose to say these things in an open ward, revealing to anyone who walks past an element of private character previously revealed only to a chosen few. Here, there is no option but to say them in a very public way, with a stranger in a nurses uniform standing just feet away, and the possibility that every syllable will carry still further. The only other option is not to say them at all.

Recently, a middle-aged man was admitted who had been involved in a very nasty smash while riding a motor-bike. Flesh is extremely soft and fragile compared to metal, and so it is no surprise that motorbike riders come off worst in any collision with a car. Often you can tell what type of motorbike was involved in the crash simply by looking at the patient's injuries. Sleek racing bikes, where the rider crouches over the petrol tank, usually deliver a patient with head injuries after a head-on smash. Old-fashioned sit-up-and-beg bikes where the rider is in a more upright position usually give us a patient whose pelvis and chest have been crushed. (Injuries characteristic to a particular type of vehicle are not unusual. Even during World War Two, it was possible to tell whether a British pilot had been flying a Hurricane or a Spitfire, simply by seeing which part of their body had been burnt by flames from the fuel line.)

But behind this crash was an even more tragic tale. The man, who was married with three children, had sold his car and bought the motorbike so that he could cut the cost of going to work and use the money saved to take his wife and children on their first family holiday. He was a poorly paid manual worker, so every penny was important, and he was prepared to endure the cold and wet weather on his bike if it meant that he could achieve a long-cherished dream.

But life doesn't always work out the way we think it should, and needless to say, by cruel circumstance he was involved in a road accident just two weeks after buying the bike. When he came to the Unit, he was very badly injured, and his chances of survival were slim. The family was devastated. They blamed themselves for the accident, reasoning that if it hadn't have been for them, he wouldn't have been tempted to sell the car and use the motorbike instead. Their anguish by the bedside was heart-breaking. His wife didn't know what to do or who to turn to. All she could see was her husband, badly injured and close to death, and she felt that it was her fault. Her children felt the same too, and in the midst of the pain of hearing that their father had been involved in an accident, you could see them blaming themselves for what had happened. It must have been a terrible feeling, and the emotion of the occasion was clear to everyone on the unit.

'We didn't need a holiday,' they said. 'We would much rather have our dad back in full health.' But it was not to be; despite all of our efforts the poor man died later that day. We knew that they would have to live with this thought for the rest of their lives, and it filled all of us with horror. Imagine having to cope with the thought, real or imagined, that you had been in some way responsible for the death of your own father.

Desperate to ease their burden, we looked around for some way of alleviating their guilt. The harsh fact was that the father was dead and now it was time to help the family come to terms with his death – especially the children, who would otherwise grow up thinking that they had caused his death. In this case, there weren't that many positive aspects to be found, so we simply tried to explain the circumstances as best he could. 'Your dad wanted you to have a holiday, and it was his decision to sell the car and buy a motorbike, not yours,' my colleague explained. It was the best he could do, but it didn't seem to have that much effect.

Much though we would like to, there is no way to shield relatives from the full effects of the death of a patient. However, I am often struck by the level of ignorance of what the process actually entails, even though it is an inevitable conclusion of everyone's life cycle. I suppose we now live in a society where we no longer have to confront many painful issues, and coping with death, like so many other things, has become someone's else's responsibility. It's a sight seldom seen, even by family members, and nowadays death usually takes place behind hospital curtains rather than at home. Life is now so sanitised that death has almost come to be regarded as unnatural.

It's no wonder therefore that one of the questions we are asked most often by relatives is: 'Tell me what it is like. What will I see?'

Death happens in many different ways. Sometimes it happens completely out of the blue, when you aren't expecting it. Perhaps the heart goes into an irregular rhythm and then stops beating completely. The alarms on the monitors will sound and the bedside nurse will call urgently for assistance. The cardiac arrest trolley is rushed to the bedside. So begins the frantic attempt to restart the heart, with cardiac massage and drugs, or by giving the patient a fairly hefty electric shock. Often there will be up to four doctors and nurses around that patient's bed, each with a different job to do: some to inject drugs, some to keep the airway free, others to pump furiously on the patient's chest. Usually this is successful, but sometimes these techniques simply fail to work and the patient slips away, death coming almost unnoticed in the midst of a flurry of activity. Finally, the team realise that there is nothing more they can do and one of them will simply say: 'It's no good. He's gone. Let's call it a day.'

However, most of the deaths on this Unit aren't like that. We know when there is nothing more we can do to keep a patient alive, and so it follows that we also know that they are going to die. It should be a peaceful death, a good death, the pain removed by sedatives, and the relatives prepared beforehand for the worst. Some call it a planned death, but in many cases, this isn't true, because there is a question that relatives ask me which I can never answer with any certainty: 'When are they going to die?'

Predicting the time that a death will occur is extremely difficult; it is easily one of the hardest factors to judge, and I can never tell a family whether it will be a few minutes, a few hours or a few days. If the patient is on a breathing machine, then usually we will reduce the oxygen level to that found in ordinary air, turn down the volume of air delivered to the equivalent of a normal breath, and stop administering the drugs which increase the strength of each heartbeat. We have withdrawn treatment because it no longer has a purpose, but we have not withdrawn care. At this stage we have moved on from treatment aimed at the survival of the patient to intensive care of a dying patient and the patient is now on their own.

Sometimes, they will stay in a steady state for hours, the heart stubbornly refusing to give up, despite overwhelming odds. But usually, over the course of a day, the heartbeat will get weaker and weaker, and we know that soon it is going to stop. With a reduced blood flow, the body's tissues aren't receiving enough oxygen, and so the skin becomes a mottled blue colour, or at least develops blue patches. It comes from the colour blood assumes when deprived of oxygen, when either the lungs don't have the capacity to absorb enough gas or the heart doesn't have the strength to pump enough blood around the body. Death won't be long now.

Death itself doesn't come in an instant; it is a gradual fading away, a weakening of a presence, so that even by watching the monitors, a family often can't tell that the patient has gone. Death is a process: it is a combination of many individual events rather than a single event in itself. It begins when unconsciousness has become irreversible and ends, finally, when every cell in the body has lost its viability. We let relatives sit for a little while after the heart has stopped, alone with their thoughts, and then one of us will go over to the bedside and say: 'Things are over now . . . She is dead.'

It is important to use the word 'dead' so that relatives who are emotional are not confused by euphemisms so often used to avoid saying a word many of us fear ourselves. I remember one situation when someone said of a patient to his wife, 'he's gone' and his distraught wife asked, 'Do you mean he's been transferred to the ward?' In her mind, she genuinely thought this was possible, even though the body of her husband lay right in front of her.

We do not stop treating a patient, even when we have decided to withdraw treatment, until we know that everyone who wants to come to say their final goodbye has been. We once had a patient whose condition deteriorated relentlessly after being admitted to the Intensive Care Unit. Most his relatives were in Ireland, and even though they had been informed that he was dying, they couldn't get to the hospital for another fourteen hours. We had already decided that further treatment was pointless, but I knew that the patient would die within minutes if the ventilator was switched off, so we kept everything going until they arrived. The Unit was very busy at the time, and to be honest, we needed the bed, but that is never an issue in these circumstances. It was very important to allow the family to see their father alive, even though he was deeply sedated. They knew they were talking to a living person, they could say their final farewells to him, and so ease the sense of bereavement. They had the comfort of knowing that they had done their duty before he died.

Knowing that a patient is dying can present relatives with a dilemma. They often feel that society expects them to be at the bedside when death happens, but at the same time they know they would rather not face the ordeal. They may be frightened, or prefer to remember the patient as they were before this moment. They may resent themselves for feeling the pressure to watch something they don't want to see. There is no shame in not wanting to be there, so we try to make it clear to everyone that sitting by the bedside is not mandatory.

Sometimes, the opposite is true. After death, the relatives may not want to leave the bedside. They find it difficult to accept that the person they knew has now gone, and that only their body is left. Everyone must learn how to cope with death in their own way in their own time, and we have a duty to care for the living as well as the dead. After a while the nurse will move a sheet over the dead patient's head, and shortly afterwards perform 'last offices', which involves washing and preparing the body. Relatives sometimes wish to see the patient afterwards, after all the tubes and machines have been removed, to see them at peace before the mortuary trolley is summoned. Hospitals are steeped in superstition and just as there is no Theatre 13, so the words 'mortuary trolley' are avoided. Instead we sometimes call the porters to say we have a 'patient for Number 9'. They come along with a special trolley with covered sides, a bit like an old-fashioned school dinner trolley – not the most subtle of vehicles. Whatever personal possessions the patients may have had with them are placed in a bag and usually given to the relatives to take home.

Six weeks after the patient's death, we write to the relatives, asking them if there is anything they would like us to explain, or any questions they would like to ask about the patient's death. People who are upset can't take in what is being said to them at that time, and so no matter how much a doctor or a nurse may tell them during a patient's stay on the Unit, there may well be things they will want to know when grief has subsided. Maybe they didn't understand why a particular treatment was given, or perhaps they want to ask again why we came to the conclusion that there was no point in carrying on. We write to them rather than waiting for them to write to us, because it lets them know that we will be glad to give them our time. Also, it removes any fear that by wanting to ask these question they might appear silly or rather strange.

I find that relatives need to be certain in their own minds that everything which could have been done to save their loved one had been done. Niggling doubts, or unanswered questions can prevent them from putting the death behind them and getting on with their own lives. Telling the relatives that they are welcome to ring the Unit at any time is the least we can do to help that process. Sometimes they will ask me, 'Is he really dead?' long after the body has been buried, or 'surely there was something else you could have done to save him?' I cast my mind back to that case just to make sure before replying: 'I'm afraid that there was nothing more we could do.'

We also invite relatives back to the Unit to speak to any of the staff who cared for that patient, or to meet whatever doctor was in charge of their treatment. Some of these meetings are very touching, and I can often see the sense of bewilderment and loss which remains on their face, and it is obvious that, while time may have passed on for the rest of us, for that person, the world has stood still.

You would think that sickness and death would unite warring families, but this isn't always the case. Once I admitted a young lad and his girlfriend to the unit after they had been involved in a pretty bad car smash. Both of them were very seriously ill, and it wasn't long before the waiting room filled up with relatives from the two families, so I went to talk to them. However, it soon became clear that there was a bloody row going on. Each set of relatives was furious with the other, and for a while I couldn't work out why. But then the true story emerged.

It turned out that the parents of the young girl had never liked her boyfriend, and regarded him as a wayward influence on their daughter. He was a bit of a tearaway, and they had always wanted her to ditch him and go out with someone more suitable. Apparently it had been the subject of numerous rows, but the girl had insisted that she loved him, and ignored their advice. Her family held him to be responsible for the accident, a view enhanced by the fact that he had been drinking and may have been well over the legal limit.

All were desperately worried about their children, but the tension was so great that it had to explode, and soon they were shouting and swearing at each other, and calling each other's child all the names under the sun. At the same time, each family knew the grief being experienced by the other. They felt guilty but angry at the same time.

We tried to make them settle their differences. 'If you care anything at all for those two young people, then you will save your arguments for another time,' I admonished, but we might just as well have saved our breath for on they went.

Finally, the argument had run its course. Everything that each side had wanted to say had been said – many, many times, and I suppose in the end they ran out of imagination. But still the two sides weren't happy, and I knew it was only a matter of time before another argument flared up, perhaps this time in the middle of the Unit. So there was only one thing for it.

We moved the boy and girl to opposite ends of the Unit, and arranged for each set of relatives to visit the unit through different doors, keeping them well away from each other. You could still see the murderous looks flashing between the two groups as they sat around each bed, but at least it prevented a punch-up. This story does not have a happy ending: the young boy recovered, but his girlfriend never regained consciousness and died a few days later.

Accidents can happen at any time – in the middle of the night or in the middle of a party – and over the years we have almost become used to having to deal with relatives who are drunk and rowdy. Occasionally, however, some of the confrontations take on a more serious hue.

One night, just after midnight, a young lad was brought in with several stab wounds to the chest and face, and also to his hands as he had tried to ward off the thrusting blade. At first we thought it was the result of a simple argument, but the true circumstances were a lot more complicated. Rumours abounded that he had been responsible for raping the sister of an opposing gang member, but we couldn't discover what the truth was. One thing was certain, however: the waiting room was rapidly filling up with thugs baying for the boy's blood and threatening to come in to finish the job someone else had only partially completed. 'Don't think that bastard is going to get away with it,' they told me. 'That shit aught to be dead.'

The boy was still alive – just – but they certainly had the muscle and the manpower to storm the Unit any time they pleased. The nurses looking after the boy were terrified. There were no locks on the Unit doors, and they knew that should the thugs decide to come in, there was little they could do to stop them. One yank at the ventilator tube, or even worse, another knife wound, would certainly kill him. The prospects for defending a patient against these thugs were not good.

Even so, all of the staff on the Unit carried on working, with some of the male nurses taking up positions near the boy's bedside. Frantic telephone calls were being made to the police, but it would be some time before they arrived, and in the meantime, things were looking nasty. And that's when the boy's relatives arrived – and set upon the thugs that had been threatening to kill him.

Other relatives, waiting and worried about their own loved one, suddenly found themselves in the middle of a fracas, surrounded by swearing louts and threats of violence. It must have been like sitting in the middle of a seething terrace of rival football hooligans.

There was only one thing for it. One of the nurses here is a very big chap, so he bravely went out to them and began to read the riot act. Meanwhile, we summoned as many big hospital porters as we could find to back him up, buying us time until the police arrived. Our staff were surprisingly effective, especially the nurse, so that by the time the boys in blue arrived things were beginning to settle down. Although there had been scuffles, no one had been seriously thumped.

Later, I wondered why they hadn't carried out their threat to finish the young boy off. These days, thugs don't hesitate to attack rival gang members in casualty, ignoring doctors' pleas to respect their attempt to make people better. The only conclusion I could come to was that invading an Intensive Care Unit was still regarded as a step too far, even for these louts. Nothing else could have prevented them from storming into the Unit, and by the time the police arrived, it would have been too late. Times like these make me glad that the best suit that I wear to work every day is more than five years old.

CHAPTER FIVE

Medicine

IT SHOULD HAVE BEEN A SIMPLE CASE but it wasn't. He was suffering from pneumococcal pneumonia – a fairly standard type of pneumonia caused by a pneumococcus bacteria. It had started as a cough, no different from any other, but as the day wore on, the man, in his mid-twenties and otherwise fit and healthy, had begun to feel worse and worse. At first his wife thought it was a particularly bad cold which would blow over with a few days' bed-rest and lots of tender loving care. But she was wrong.

The next day, his condition had deteriorated considerably, and he could barely breathe, so strong was the rapidly increasing bacterial infection attacking his lungs. At last, there was nothing for it but to bring him to hospital.

It didn't take long to diagnose the problem. An X-ray showed how badly his lungs were affected, and a microscopic examination of secretions from his chest quickly revealed the identity of the bug which was causing the problem. Later, a bacterial culture showed that the bacteria was sensitive to penicillin, so that a course of injections of this antibiotic would rapidly wipe out the entire pneumococcus population which had infected his lungs thus easing his problems.

As well as attacking the lung tissue, bacteria also produce poisons which can have a catastrophic effect on the human body. When the young man came to us, the antibiotic treatment had probably already wiped out the population of bacteria, but now his body was having to contend with the high concentrations of poisons left behind.

Already, he was beginning to show signs of a severe reaction against the toxins, called Systemic Inflammatory Response Syndrome – SIRS for short. This is a very difficult condition to treat.

In effect, the body declares war on itself. Registering the presence of high concentrations of poisons, the liver concludes that the body is under attack, and the patient's immune system releases powerful chemicals which are designed to kill off the invading organism. It's the body's equivalent of a last-ditch measure to ward off severe infections. Unfortunately, the chemicals released are so strong that they also damage the body's own tissues, especially delicate cells such as are found in the lungs and kidneys. It's a bit like flushing bleach through your arteries to get rid of an infection. Yes, it might work, but only at the expense of destroying everything else in its path. Biological and chemical warfare rolled into one, with all their inherent imprecision on the battlefield.

The young man was now very seriously ill. In time, his body would clear the pneumococcus toxin by itself, but time wasn't on his side. The reaction his body was undergoing already carried a mortality rate of over 50 per cent – a figure which was becoming even higher as each vital organ failed in turn. The chance of predicting correctly the fall of a coin was already higher than his chance of recovery.

One of my colleagues was on call that weekend and it was already late into the night. Large volumes of fluid were being fed into the patient's veins by drips, and high concentrations of oxygen were pumped into his lungs by a ventilator set at the highest pressure that could be tolerated without causing even more injury to his already damaged lungs. Even so, we could see his condition deteriorate hour by hour, and so could his young wife as she kept vigil by his bedside. Already his kidneys had failed, so now his blood was being cleaned by a haemo-filtration machine. Nothing was working, and death looked simply a matter of time.

If we could only buy some of that precious time, we could save this man's life. The haemo-filtration would speed up the process of eliminating the toxins, quelling the reason for the body's potentially lethal adverse reaction to the infection. Keeping the patient alive long enough would allow the body to, in effect, heal itself. The pneumococcus was already dead and the toxin levels had begun to fall: the road to recovery was within sight. We were so close – and yet so far. Could we hold off the worst effects of the reaction long enough to allow this man to recover?

The levels of oxygen in the man's bloodstream was falling rapidly. His damaged lungs were no longer able to absorb enough of the vital gas to saturate the blood, even though he was now being fed 100 per cent pure oxygen at maximum pressure through the ventilator. Soon, a point would come where not enough oxygen was reaching the brain, and deprived of this important element, brain tissue would start to die. This meant that even if the patient did eventually survive, he would almost certainly be severely handicapped.

It was so frustrating. Here was a man who should have been fit and healthy, who should have made a fairly straightforward recovery from a serious but treatable disease. The toxin levels were falling rapidly as the filter cleansed the blood, and recovery was almost within our grasp, a mere fingertip away. One man's life was slipping away, as my colleague stood by the bedside, wondering what else could possibly be done to buy that little bit of extra time which might make all the difference. And that's when he took the brave decision to try something that had never been done before.

After previous unsuccessful attempts to treat patients in this situation, we had often wondered what else we could do to increase oxygen levels in the blood to a level sufficient to keep a patient with damaged lung function alive long enough to allow them to recover. Was there any way of increasing blood saturation quickly and easily in situations where there isn't enough time to transfer the patient to special centres which can artificially raise blood oxygen levels using specialist techniques?

In theory, a method based on the same principle as that of the haemo-filtration machine should be able to achieve this. Instead of a fluid drawing off impurities from the blood through a thin membrane, it could be possible one day to have a portable machine which would allow oxygen to pass across the membrane into the blood. In the meantime, we didn't have such a piece of equipment, and the haemo-filtration machine was designed to run on fluid and in reverse of anything we had envisaged.

Our conversations had been based on conjecture, pure theory discussed over a cup of coffee in the office. Yet, here was a man who was dying – if only such a machine existed at that moment. That's when my colleague decided to act, he knew it probably wouldn't work but there was nothing to lose. He explained to the man's distraught wife what he intended to do as best and as quickly as he could under the circumstances, explaining the considerable risk involved. Knowing that her husband was about to die, she gave her consent. She was being offered a chance and, however slim it seemed, she had to take it.

He quickly disconnected the tube carrying the cleansing fluid out of the haemo-filtration machine, and replaced it with the pipe from the oxygen supply. Now, instead of fluid, pure oxygen gas was coursing through the machine, separated from the patient's bloodstream only by the thinnest of thin membranes.

It was a crazy thing to do. The potential for killing the patient was enormous. Had the gas-flow burst the membrane, it would have sent large bubbles of oxygen surging straight into the patient's blood stream, with lethal consequences. And what was the point? We had been through the calculations many times before – and they just didn't seem to work. The flow of blood through the machine was so small in comparison to the body's total volume of blood that any increase in oxygen saturation would have been insignificant. No more than 500 millilitres of blood was flowing through the haemo-filtration machine every minute, and even successful techniques, using equipment specifically designed for that purpose, use a flow of several litres of blood per minute. The physics just didn't add up.

Much to everyone's surprise it did work. Looking up at the monitor, everyone could see that the level of oxygen in the patient's blood had increased significantly. The young man who had been at the point of death would now have the chance to recover.

Even at a time of such pressure, my colleague recorded all the necessary measurements. This data would be required for analysis later, in order to explain what had happened. The next day we all pawed over this data: how on earth could the necessary volume of oxygen needed to raise the oxygen levels in the blood, be absorbed through such a meagre flow through the haemo-filtration unit?

Later, we conducted tests to find out why this unorthodox technique had worked. We decided that the only possible explanation was that the membrane had allowed micro-bubbles of oxygen to pass directly into the patient's blood, and these had immediately been absorbed by the red cells which carry an oxygen-loving chemical called haemoglobin. The effect had been rather like a mini-lung, increasing the oxygen saturation in the blood to a point where the body's vital organs could obtain a sufficient supply to prevent death. The technique, although risky, had allowed a faster and therefore far greater rate of oxygen absorption than previous methods.

Ultrasound investigations confirmed our hypothesis, so we wrote up our exciting discovery as a scientific report and sent it off to various medical journals. Publication would let other doctors know what we had done and why it had worked, allowing others to develop the technique still further. Further research into the method would mean that other patients in similar circumstances would benefit from our 'last chance' technique.

But not one journal would publish our findings. Each editor gave the same reason. The technique was considered far too risky. Yes, it had worked – this time. But the editors felt that printing the article in a journal would only encourage more doctors to engage in what could very well be a fatal course of action, bringing death to the patient – and landing the doctor in court. They felt that publication would be irresponsible, so our findings have never seen the light of day.

I can see what they mean. The method was used in desperation and is undeniably very dangerous. But the fact that it worked, even if only on one occasion, surely means that it is worthy of further investigation. We were very disappointed that no one saw fit to bring the method to a wider audience. Publication would have raised the subject overnight with a plethora of experts, each able to query our findings and suggest alternative reasons why it had such a significant effect. Above all, it would have allowed the method to be subjected to proper scrutiny, and accepted or rejected on merit. It certainly would have resulted in an improved understanding of what we had done. Nevertheless we have no doubt about the value of this discovery. While it would only ever be applied in a dire emergency, where the patient is going to die anyway, we would have no hesitation in giving the technique another try should similar circumstances ever arise.

Thanks to this courageous decision, the patient survived the night. The next day he began to get better. We stopped the filter and later we were able to take him off the ventilator and he made a full recovery. There is no doubt that he owes his life to my colleague's decision. I can think of other doctors who might have wondered if they should attempt such a drastic remedy, but who would have hesitated, deterred by the real possibility of being sued if it were to go wrong.

Later, when the patient fully recovered, he returned to the unit to give us his thanks. He knew that his life had rested on a truly experimental method.

Sometimes it is necessary to use equipment and drugs in ways which differ significantly from the manufacturers' recommendations. Administering drugs to critically ill people is a different science to giving the same drug to someone who is not so ill. Seriously ill people show a different reaction to drugs than their more healthy counterparts. The correct dose for a normal person may be too much for someone who has an impaired liver function or heart failure. Sick people may not be able to metabolise a drug as quickly or as efficiently as a healthy person, so the effects can often be unpredictable. This sometimes means that guidelines on dosage and frequency of a particular drug, established by manufacturers after exhaustive tests, have to be drastically revised. We have to use our own experience and strict observation to judge just how much of each drug is appropriate to each patient.

In addition, we may also use drugs in ways for which they were never intended, but there is scientific evidence to suggest that they may be beneficial to the patient's welfare. An example is a particular antibiotic designed to combat bacterial infection which is usually only given where a specific infection needs to be treated – often, for instance, to treat a resistant pneumonia. Unfortunately it often produces diarrhoea as a side effect. Recently we have found that this antibiotic used in very small doses also helps maintain the movements of a patient's intestines when they would otherwise come to a standstill. It keeps the gut working, which means that the patient can still absorb nutrients from food efficiently and easily. This enables us to feed them by stomach tube – an easier, safer, and cheaper method than a liquid drip directly into their veins. Keeping the gut in good condition also reduces the risk of a break in the intestine wall, which would allow infection to spill from the gut into the bloodstream, provoking the systematic inflammatory response syndrome. So all in all, this drug is an invaluable tool in our battle to get seriously ill people well again.

Yet, its use in this way is outside the guidelines for using the drug which were laid down when its licence was first granted by medical authorities; at the time it was never envisaged that this could be a possible side benefit, and so this use was never tested before the drug was given official approval. The consultant must take full responsibility for such unlicensed use.

There is a strict procedure which must be followed before such use can be justified; this involves presenting the facts to a specially selected panel called the Ethical Committee. Members of this panel include scientific experts, legal advisors, doctors, nurses, members of religious orders and a representative of the lay public. They consider the strength of existing evidence that the treatment could be beneficial, and the potential for causing harm. They also ensure that the treatment will be used in such a way that, when the results are examined, it can be clearly shown that the benefit was not just a chance effect. This means using the drug in a standard way each time as part of a properly designed scientific study. Finally, and most importantly, the Ethical Committee ensure that the information given to the relatives is full and fair and that their written consent is obtained.

Such scientific studies are an important part of our work in Intensive Care. It is only by these methods that we can safely advance our knowledge to the benefit of all critically ill patients. To ignore this procedure could lead to the accusation that we are deliberately ignoring the wealth of medical guidelines which through experiment have determined what is and what is not a safe way to use this drug. In other words, if anything ever went wrong, we could be sued for negligence.

Many of our patients are sedated for very long periods of time, sometimes several weeks. Despite the presence of caring, sympathetic nurses on the unit, we have to use sedation for both humanitarian and medical reasons. For instance, sedation reduces the mental stress of having a tube constantly in the throat when a patient is connected to a ventilator, and it reduces the fear experienced by many patients who are surrounded by many frightening sights and sounds. Sedation can also reduce pressure in the brain, and with it the chance of further injury to an already brain injured patient.

Unfortunately, though, there are very few drugs which have been approved for the specific needs of Intensive Care. We sometimes need to keep patients sedated for weeks at a time but most sedatives are only supposed to be administered to a patient for short periods of time – usually for no longer than a few hours. Although their license may cover this type of use, we have to keep a careful eye out for any long-term side effects of drugs on our patients. There is little commercial incentive for pharmaceutical companies to perform the endless tests required by the licensing authorities in order for them to approve drugs to be used in all the ways we may need to use them. In a small, highly specialised area such as Intensive Care, the massive financial investment for such exploration gets little return so we often don't get our specialised drugs.

Although we have a considerable amount of accumulated evidence from fellow Intensive Care specialists on the effects of such drugs over a prolonged period, we are sometimes pressing ahead into unchartered territory. When a patient's life is at risk, we will often have no option. If it works well we do it. However, there have been situations where a seemingly ideal drug, that has been administered to many thousands of critically ill patients over several years, is found to have a serious side effect. One such drug was used for long-term sedation for several years, before a careful study showed that it suppressed the release of a vital stress hormone, and was possibly associated with a higher mortality rate than was predicted. We all stopped using it for this purpose overnight.

Using drugs in this way is done for the best possible reasons. If my life hung in the balance, I would like to think that doctors treating me were prepared to pursue any line of treatment which could make a difference. However, there is one huge disadvantage. Unless procedures have been carefully followed we may be wide open to legal action, even though we have acted with the best intention. Faced with a sharp lawyer, and irrefutable evidence that we had wilfully ignored manufacturer's guidelines on the use of their drugs, a jury, unversed in the ways of Intensive Care, might quickly come to the conclusion that we had acted against the patient's interests, even though the opposite was true. It is essential, under these circumstances, for us to maintain good communication with the relatives of the patient being treated. We must obtain their consent to use drugs in unusual ways, and we must be careful to explain both the advantages of using a drug in a particular way, and the possible side effects. Consents are carefully recorded but, even so, a relative's consent to pursue a certain line of treatment is not a water-tight defence in a court of law: the only defence would be that we have followed the correct procedure for a scientific study or proof that the usage was accepted practice in the specialist area of Intensive Care, or, finally that as doctors, we were acting in the best interests of the patient. Whichever way, we would need experts in our field to give supporting evidence on our behalf and that evidence would have to be more convincing than that provided by the other side.

Fortunately, in this country, such legal battle are unusual. Relatives know that we have done our best to save a patient's life, and see our unusual deployment of drugs as yet another attempt to leave no stone unturned.

However, I have little doubt that as the public becomes more familiar with the procedures of Intensive Care, public expectations will rise. It will be taken for granted that for many conditions anyone who goes there should automatically recover. Certain conditions we treat will come to be regarded as routine illnesses, and therefore treatable in every instance. Woe betide the doctor whose patient should die, even though they have tried their best to keep them alive. Questions will be asked, and inquiries held with the implied message that death has occurred through either negligence or incompetence. This seems to have happened in the other areas of health care, so why not Intensive Care? In the years ahead, I expect that this area of medicine will be subject to legal challenges in all sorts of areas.

In my view, such a state of affairs would greatly lower the standard of care currently available to Intensive Care patients. At the moment, my colleagues and I can, in exceptional circumstances, take risks in a last desperate attempt to save a life. Sometimes it may not work, but it is still worth trying. However, if the heavy hand of the law hung over us all, few doctors would be willing to put the patient's interests before their own. If it came to a question of trying out a new technique to save a patient and risking a lawsuit, everyone would, naturally, play safe, even if this meant letting the patient die. It would be impossible for my colleague to do what he did with the haemo-filtration machine. The fact that the patient survived and went on to lead a long and happy life would be no defence. As soon as you get into what is called protective medicine, you watch your back.

All accidents are avoidable, but they do happen, and medicine is no exception. All of us, no matter what we do for a living, have at some time done something wrong. We may have experienced a near shave in our cars, or perhaps even been involved in a crash or collision where damage has been caused. Under these circumstances, we will all call it an accident. Doctors and nurses suffer from human frailties just like the rest of mankind. Mistakes inevitably occur from time to time, despite rigorous controls. However, there may come a time when nothing less than perfection will be accepted. We're all human, and even with the highest standards, things will sometimes occur which with hindsight or better judgement should not have happened.

There must be a better way of dealing with human failings than dragging good people, who have acted with the best of motives, through the besmearing ordeal of a courtroom. I appreciate that enquiries must be held to see if there is room for improving accepted practices to reduce the chance of a similar event ever happening again, but litigation is surely not always the best way forward. The present system provides the victims of such medical accidents little option because, in order to gain deserved financial compensation, they have to destroy the reputation of a doctor – and it's all because of one slip.

When treating very ill people the margin for error is very slim. They don't have the same resilience as more healthy people, so that even a small disruption of their circumstances may be fatal.

One such accident occurred when I was a junior doctor. The consultant surgeon, a consultant anaesthetist, and a senior registrar were examining a patient who had just had a major operation and who was having severe problems breathing. We decided to put him on to a ventilator to help him breathe. This would tide him over the worst of his illness until he had recovered sufficient strength and health to breathe for himself once again.

The ventilator was already prepared and assembled, and had previously been checked in the routine manner. I watched as my two more senior Intensive Care colleagues set to work. They attached a drip to the patient's arm and then injected an anaesthetic drug into the drip. Then they inserted a tube through his open mouth, into his windpipe, and tied it in place with cotton tapes. The machine was started up, and we heard the familiar whoosh as the air was pumped. The oxygen concentration, pressures and tidal volumes were checked and were quite normal.

Two minutes later the patient suddenly had a cardiac arrest. Alarms on the monitors bleeped furiously as his heart stopped, summoning help from other parts of the Unit. There wasn't a moment to lose, so we sprang into action. One of us administered heart massage, another prepared drugs to stimulate the heart, while yet another charged up the defibrillator, a machine which delivers a hefty electric shock, kick starting the heart into action again. While these preparations were being made, the patient had quickly been taken off the ventilator and 'bagged', which means neat oxygen was blown into his lung by hand, using a collapsible rubber bag at the side of the machine, rather like the inner tube of a leather football.

After a few moments, his heart spontaneously re-started, and we all breathed a sigh of relief. It was assumed that the cardiac arrest had occurred because of the man's poor state of health. Low levels of oxygen in the blood can put an increased strain on an already weak heart. It is not uncommon for ill patients to die from a heart attack, even though the reason for their true illness lies elsewhere. The crisis was over, so once again artificial ventilation was started. No sooner had the ventilator been reconnected when the patient suffered a cardiac arrest, for the second time. Again, the patient was bagged and cardiac massage was started, and he spontaneously recovered after a few seconds. We carefully listened to his chest in order to check for the possibility of a condition called pneumothorax, but all seemed well, so he was reconnected to the breathing machine. Only then did we realise that something was wrong. It was actually the nurse who worked out what it was. Watching carefully, he noticed that the chest didn't move as it should have done, as the air entered his lungs, even though all the gauges and dials were telling us that everything was working properly.

The tubes from the ventilator had been assembled in the wrong way. A one-way valve controlling the flow of air from the ventilator to the patient had been put in the wrong way round. Instead of allowing air to flow from the machine into the patient's lungs and out again, it simply diverted the vital flow of air straight to the air bag by the side of the ventilator, starving the patient of oxygen. It meant that everyone was fooled into thinking that the machine was working. Because the resistance of the bag to inflation mirrored almost exactly those of the patient's lungs, gauges on the machine showed that it was delivering the right volume of air at the right pressure and frequency. As the bag expanded and contracted, it also fooled the machine into thinking that air was indeed returning to it having already been used by the patient. In fact, no such thing was happening. The cardiac arrest had occurred because we had prevented this man from breathing by connecting him to the ventilator. It was an error which so easily could have cost him his life, and it was only spotted because one of the nurses checked to see if the man's chest was moving as he was being connected to the ventilator for a third time.

Checking for chest movements is one of the golden rules when connecting a patient to a ventilator, and this case made me appreciate how such golden rules evolve. And I remember thinking that if a mistake can be made by not one, but three senior doctors like those attending that patient, then it could happen to anyone.

Ventilators have since been redesigned to make it unlikely that this particular mistake could occur now but there is always the constant danger of something else going wrong. In these days of high technology, with complicated equipment telling you all sorts of measurements, it is very easy to have too much faith in machinery and not enough in your own eyes. It was a lesson I haven't forgotten.

We use very powerful drugs on Intensive Care. Often these have to be administered in small but constant amounts over time rather than a single injection so that their effect is continuous. A conventional injection would exaggerate the effects as the initial surge of the drug hits the bloodstream and then dies away with time, so instead, we use motor-driven syringes, called infusion pumps, which inject the drug at a steady rate, so that the levels of drug in the patient's body remain constant. This is particularly useful for administering constant low doses of sedatives and tran-quillisers to keep the patient sedated to a constant level. But occasionally things can go wrong.

I remember one day hearing one of the nurses calling urgently for help. A mechanical syringe had gone berserk. Inside was 50 millilitres of a powerful anaesthetic, which should have been ad-ministered at the rate of three millilitres per hour. Instead despite the pump being set correctly, it had gone mad and injected the entire dose in a matter of seconds. As a result, the blood pressure of an already sick patient was sinking like a stone.

My initial thoughts were 'That's it. There is no way this

patient is going to survive.' Of all the patients it could have happened to, it had to be this one, who could least survive such a mishap. Already I was wondering of how I was going to break the news to her relatives that someone they loved had died because of a faulty machine.

However, this was not a time for dithering. Quickly, we pumped the woman full of drugs to stimulate her heart and keep her blood pressure up. In my mind I could see inquiries, coroner's inquests and an endless stream of questions and accusations and tears. How could this have happened? What had gone wrong? Why did this woman have to die in such a futile manner? And in Intensive Care of all places, a place where her relatives had a right to expect that she would receive the best care possible.

She was totally unresponsive for many hours. The drug had totally suppressed her brain activity and although there was some response to the stimulant drugs, her blood pressure was still very low. For a long time, it was touch and go. All that night we waited, hoping for signs of an improvement. The next morning she started showing some real response to the treatment, but we had to wait another forty-eight hours before we could be sure there was no residual brain damage. Miraculously, she was fine, and soon she was back to her admittedly poor original state of health.

There followed a thorough inquiry. Every infusion pump of this type in the unit was taken out of use while the offending machine was taken apart and examined in minute detail to find out what had caused such a near-fatal malfunction. The manufacturer of the pump was informed, and a hazard warning issued to all other users in the country. It soon became apparent that this was not an isolated incident: similar accidents had occurred in other units. As a result, the design of every infusion pump in the country was modified. It meant a change in technology – and a vast increase in price.

As a consultant on an Intensive Care Unit, I feel I have a much easier time than the rest of my staff when it comes to facing the consequences of things going wrong. In my role as a manager, I usually get to hear about things that have happened rather than experiencing them at first-hand. It is the junior doctors and nurses who are most exposed to such accidents and are required to act quickly and decisively when such events occur.

Medical students in this country receive very little training in the techniques of Intensive Care. It seems paradoxical that here, in the Queen's Medical Centre, we have a regular attachment of students from the medical school at Grenoble. French medical students have a long attachment to our Unit, because Intensive Care is considered to be a very important part of the training of young modern doctors all over Europe. Yet here in Nottingham, with one of the best medical schools in the country, and one of the best Intensive Care Units, our own students are attached to the Unit for less than one day during their week long introduction to anaesthetics. In this time, they might get an afternoon – if they are lucky – to look around the unit and see what Intensive Care is all about. Otherwise, they have very little exposure to this particular field of medicine. This situation is no different in most other British medical schools.

This system of training, almost designed to encourage ignorance about an important new speciality, continues after they qualify. Most of the junior doctors who come to this Unit do so only as part of their training in other areas. Out of the five junior staff who are on the Unit at present, three are training to be anaesthetists, one to be a physician and the fifth to work in Accident and Emergency. Few of the juniors we see want a career as an Intensive Care specialist. The few who do will have to carve out a suitable training for themselves.

Unlike most other medical disciplines, there is no formal Intensive Care career path that ambitious young doctors can pursue designed specifically to make them experts in this particular field. Instead, they will have to follow the same torturous route that my colleagues and I followed, to gain the necessary experience to work in a busy unit like this one.

They will have to work out for themselves what skills are essential, and then apply to whatever hospital can give them a job where they can pick up one of those skills. Once they have experience in one area, then it's time to move on, to another job offering another skill at another hospital. Finally, the sum of all those different techniques will qualify them to work in an Intensive Care Unit. They will need to have gained a good grounding in general medicine, working as a physician to build up a sound knowledge of a wide variety of conditions. They will also need to be skilled in anaesthesia, simply because so many of the really important things that have to be done in a hurry to save a patient's life involve techniques taught during the study of anaesthesia. Keeping an unconscious patient's airway clear involves being able to pass a plastic tube quickly and accurately into the windpipe and administer anaesthetics safely. Fine tubes called cannulae have to be placed in the patient's veins, sometimes passed through the chambers of the heart. These are all procedures that anaesthetists follow daily. There is no other medical discipline where doctors can learn these particular skills.

In addition, successful Intensive Care specialists have to know about heart medicine, lung medicine, kidney medicine and neurosurgery. You have to build your career carefully; take advantage of suitable opportunities and plan your next move. It's a bit like playing a game of chess. Few doctors drift into Intensive Care by accident. However this path is becoming more difficult to follow as areas of speciality now require specific forms of training, so there are fewer opportunities available to doctors wanting to piece together different kinds of experience.

This situation also has repercussions for patients in wards outside the Intensive Care Unit. The general lack of understanding amongst doctors about what Intensive Care involves and has to offer is a major cause of delay in patients being referred to this unit at a sufficiently early stage of their illness. Time is often crucial; the earlier we see a patient, the better chance we have of successfully treating them. Unfortunately, it sometimes happens that, by the time we are finally called in, the patient is so ill that admitting them to Intensive Care would be pointless. There is no longer anything we can do to help, yet a simple telephone call earlier in the proceedings from a ward doctor could have made all the difference.

It seems extraordinary that Intensive Care, such a specialised area of medicine, should have to depend upon the limitless enthusiasm of doctors who are willing to put up with such an arduous route to their chosen career. It's an active disincentive to becoming an Intensive Care specialist, limiting our intake of new talent to those dogged enough to tackle these hurdles, or whose circumstances will allow them to do so. Hopefully it won't always be so. Plans are afoot to create a new faculty of medicine dedicated entirely to the techniques of Intensive Care medicine.

Although many of the junior doctors who come to the Unit enjoy the experience, some of them do so under sufferance. They are on attachment here for between two and six months, usually seconded from another speciality where they may ultimately want to work. They would avoid Intensive Care if they could. However, many courses such as anaesthetics cannot be completed unless each candidate has successfully completed a stay on an Intensive Care Unit.

Many are frightened by the prospect of their first day on the Unit. Some may feel they have been flung in at the deep end, expected to make important decisions without having the experience to back them up.

Unfortunately, it is often true that they do lack experience. This places a heavy burden on the consultants who must supervise them closely. Nurses have a minimum of one month when they come on to the unit in a supernumerary capacity and can simply shadow a senior colleague until they are well versed in the basic procedures of Intensive Care. Even then, they are strictly supervised, and allowed to do only the most simple tasks for months after their arrival.

Junior doctors don't even have that simple luxury. We have an information package which is sent to them shortly before they join the Unit. It's intended as a simple introduction to Intensive Care, preparing them for the sort of thing they may well find upon their arrival, and telling them what their role will be. They are also encouraged to visit the Unit before their attachment, to have a look around, giving them some idea of how the unit operates and who is who.

At least that's the theory. In practice it doesn't work like that. Junior doctors can't be expected to learn everything they can about their stay on the Intensive Care Unit in their spare time, in addition to fulfilling their commitments to their present job. It's hardly surprising therefore that most junior doctors turn up on a Monday morning for their first day in Intensive Care not knowing the slightest thing about the Unit, or the staff. Although they have received the information pack, they may not have got around to reading it.

All being well, they will have a brief introduction to the Unit on their first morning, and perhaps a general discussion of some of the techniques being used. But if the Unit is busy and there is no one available to carry out that introduction, then they will have to roll up their sleeves and get going right from the moment they arrive. It's a case of saying: 'Here is your patient, now get on with it.'

The day starts at 8.30am with a consultant ward round. Problems that have occurred during the night are discussed and the patient's care planned for the day. After this has been completed all the patients are examined from head to toe and the results of tests are scrutinised. All this is recorded in the case notes, as are any instructions from other specialist teams who are also involved in the care of a patient. There are then practical procedures to carry out. After a short break for coffee there is another consultant round – this time to review progress against the plan now that more information is available. After a short break for lunch there may be some time for teaching, but all the time there are new patients to see and more procedures to perform. Usually there is then a quick round to see that all the jobs are done, and to discover any unexpected problems. Later, at about 7pm there is yet another round, this time to hand over information on the day's events to the on-call consultant and junior doctor who will be on duty for the night.

Like junior doctors in many other areas of medicine, they are expected to become instant experts in Intensive Care, and often there isn't any margin for error. Fortunately there are major changes in the training of junior doctors around the corner. Already the hours that a junior doctor has to work have reduced considerably. Our doctors work for a maximum of 56 hours per week, and we have a shift system so that doctors do not have to work for hours and hours at a time. There is also an overlapping period between each shift, where doctors can hand over their cases to the next doctor on duty. Other countries, such as Australia and the United States, have specific training for doctors who want to specialise in Intensive Care, in the form of a 'Fellowship Training Programme'. This leads to a specialised postgraduate qualification in the field. Gradually, we are moving towards a similar sort of programme in this country, but I, like many of my colleagues, feel the pace of change is pitifully slow.

As a Junior doctor, your first day is certainly a terrifying prospect. All around you are very ill people. Many are close to death, some are going to die no matter what you do, and still more are on the verge of recovery. Most are very unstable with conditions which can change at a moment's notice. In the day time, it is possible to keep up a brave exterior. There's always a consultant present to lend advice, so that inexperienced doctors can at least feel confident that help is just a quick shout away should anything go wrong. But at night, the Intensive Care Unit can be a

103

very lonely place for a young doctor wondering just what the coming hours will hold. The welfare of every patient will depend directly upon what he or she decides to do; the pressure is immense.

In practice, help is usually close at hand. The nurses on this Unit are very experienced specialists in Intensive Care. They will usually have a very good idea of exactly what should be done in an entire range of emergencies. It simply requires the doctor to have the good sense and humility to consider any advice they may proffer. On this Unit, a consultant is available seven days a week, twenty-four hours a day. All of the five consultants who work on this Unit are immediately available both by mobile telephone and by Air Call beep. It's a belt and braces arrangement so that if one system doesn't work, then we still have another communications system as a back up.

The relationship between junior doctors and nurses on this Unit is an interesting one. All doctors are taught to have confidence in their own abilities; you have to have a lot of self belief to do the job well. The expectation that you are going to make someone well requires a high degree of certainty that you have the correct skills and knowledge for the job. It doesn't do the patient much good if a doctor has an attack of the jitters halfway through an operation. Then again, neither does it do them much good if the doctor's confidence dwarfs his true capabilities.

On this Unit, we try to give our junior staff the confidence in their abilities which is vital for us all if we are to perform at our peak, but we are careful not to allow them to become over confident. Their relationship with the nurses plays an important part in that strategy. Like it or not, junior doctors who come on to this unit have to accept that many of the nurses working alongside them, although not medically qualified, will certainly know more about the practical aspects of managing critically ill patients than they do. Asking for their advice is a doctor's first exercise in swallowing pride. Usually they are only too grateful to look to such support but sometimes it can be a difficult meal to digest.

As a junior doctor during my first attachment, I was only too thankful for the advice and guidance of the Intensive Care nurses. They knew so much and saved me from making many mistakes. All of my consultant colleagues have had the same experience, and most of the juniors too will gladly take advice from their nursing colleagues. However, some doctors have difficulty in accepting the nurse's role in Intensive Care.

Sometimes, my consultant colleagues and I can spot such attitude problems during one of the numerous daily ward rounds, where the junior is expected to describe what they have done and why they have done it. However, a much better guide to a junior doctor's performance comes from the nurses who stay with each patient for the entire duration of their shift. After years of experience, they will have a fairly good idea of how that patient should be treated, and so I expect them to pick up any undue junior doctor arrogance standing in the way of sound medical action.

I always tell junior doctors that nurses have an inalienable right to contact the Intensive Care consultant about the treatment given to a patient at any time of the day or night. Any nurse, no matter how junior, can telephone the consultant on call and ask them to give an opinion if they are not happy about the decisions being made by a junior doctor. In practice, this very rarely occurs and it tends to be only the more senior nurses who ever have to take this step. They will contact me at home, and tactfully suggest that since the Unit is very busy, I might like to come in to help the junior doctor review the situation. When I arrive, they will take me to one side and explain that the junior doctor is a little at sea with one particular patient and hasn't taken kindly to advice from more experienced nursing colleagues.

I never make it clear to the junior doctor that a nurse has called me in. It would only erode a working relationship, making an already difficult situation even worse. Instead, I make some excuse about 'just passing by ' and then seize the opportunity to examine how the junior has dealt with each case so far. Looking at the patient's notes, I will make up my own mind about what is the right course of action to be taken. If the treatment I decide upon happens to coincide with what the nurse has been saying all along, no mention is ever made of the fact; instead, the entire conversation takes place as if I have been totally unaware that there ever has been any difference of approach. Satisfied that everything is now under control, I leave the Unit, and let them get on with it. It's up to the doctor to decide how to deal with the fact that the nurse has been urging the right course of action all along.

However, there have been many occasions when the junior doctor has been right and the nurses have been wrong. As I say to all of the juniors on this Unit: 'You should always listen to what is being said and consider that it is probably right, but not necessarily right. You are the doctor, and at the end of the day, you must make up your own mind about what to do. If there is any doubt at all, then contact the consultant on call whatever the time.'

A good Intensive Care doctor must be able to remain very calm under pressure. While a certain degree of control during an emergency can be taught, and certainly comes with experience, in the long run, the ability to remain cool during an emergency usually boils down to the personality of the individual. A doctor who cannot perform effectively in stressful situations is a recipe for disaster.

There is also another characteristic vital to good Intensive Care. Despite an air of calm, every Intensive Care doctor must have a keenly developed sense of urgency which makes them realise the importance of taking the right action there and then, not sitting around for half an hour thinking about it. If something has to be done, then it has to be done quickly. Time is a luxury our patients can't afford. Speed of action is also something that can be taught, to some extent but in some cases, a tendency to sluggishness goes with the junior doctor's character and is impervious to change. Since most of the junior doctors who come on attachment to this Unit are merely doing so as part of their training in another medical discipline, we don't have any control over the calibre of junior doctor we receive. Inevitably, there are those less suited to Intensive Care than others.

It is a horrific feeling to be confronted with your first really big decision, knowing that the patient has to be treated quickly, but feeling that you don't have the knowledge or the confidence to do the right thing. It's a feeling that I remember well from my own days as a junior. All eyes around that bed are looking at you, waiting on you to call the shots. Often you will know exactly what to do in theory, but putting it into practice with only minutes to spare can be a nerve-bursting experience. I'm sure most junior doctors feel like this at some stage during their attachment to Intensive Care. With most junior doctors, that sense of unease is reduced with each successful diagnosis but even so it may not disappear entirely.

Some of the junior doctors I see find it difficult to cope with the endless series of ethical dilemmas they have to face constantly, day after day. The stress of being exposed to very tragic circumstances time after time takes its toll.

Occasionally, we do get the odd junior doctor who is totally unsuitable to work in Intensive Care. It doesn't happen often, maybe once or twice every two or three years. Under these circumstances, our primary responsibility is to the patients. If I feel that it is dangerous to leave this particular individual on the unit, then they will have to go. There is no other alternative. This is done after discussion with themselves and the training body of whatever discipline they have chosen to follow. It is a process called counselling, which is a very polite way of saying that they're not suitable to work in Intensive Care.

It is not necessarily a lifetime ban. They may be able to return to the unit once they have gained a little more experience elsewhere, giving them a sounder basis for the rigours of working on this unit.

I feel a great sympathy for the junior doctors who work here. The present system isn't fair on them. Working under continual pressure and downright fear during a short attachment to Intensive Care undoubtedly puts off some junior doctors from later pursuing a career in this speciality. Most leave their attachment with a sense of relief, saying they are glad to have done it, but even more glad when it is over.

However, there is another crucial reason why some junior doctors may feel that a life as an Intensive Care specialist is not for them. Occasionally they feel that a patient's death has occurred because of something they have or have not done. Such a feeling can be too much to bear.

Many of the techniques employed in this unit, as in other areas of the health service, are inherently risky. For instance, placing a measuring device inside a patient to measure the output of their heart involves passing a tube, called a Swan Ganz catheter, through the heart. This can be a dangerous procedure, especially in very sick patients. The heart has been known to stop, and sometimes can be very difficult to restart. Very rarely resuscitation will fail and the patient will die. What makes these circumstances even more painful is the clear and unavoidable link between the doctor's actions and the patient's death. There is no doubt that had that procedure not been carried out, that patient may well still be alive. The fact that the technique was being used for the best possible reason – to provide a vital supply of information essential to the management of the patient's primary condition – provides no solace. Often, in your own mind, you killed that patient.

107

Sooner or later, no matter how experienced a doctor may be in the ways of Intensive Care, they will, according to the law of averages, come across such a complication. It is difficult for any of us to rationalise the tragedy in our own minds. When it happens to a junior doctor, perhaps carrying out the technique on their own for the first time, during their first few weeks on an Intensive Care attachment, the effects can be devastating.

A similar complication can occur when inserting an endotracheal tube – the main plastic tube which runs from the ventilator into the patient's windpipe. Sometimes this tube becomes blocked and has to be changed, or it may have simply come out as the patient moves around the bed. Getting it back into place, so that it goes down the windpipe instead of into the patient's stomach, can be surprisingly difficult, and there isn't much time to get things right. All of the time that tube is out, the patient is most likely being deprived of oxygen, and in very ill people, a cardiac arrest will follow much sooner rather than later.

I know how these junior doctors must feel, because I too have gone through these experiences, and know what it is like to be utterly afraid, seeing someone in front of me about to die as a result of my actions.

Since they are unconscious and unable to move for themselves, most of our patients have to be moved every two hours to prevent them from getting pressure sores. Usually, great care is taken to ensure than none of the many tubes and monitoring lines attached to each patient is disturbed by this process. But one day, a momentary lapse in a nurse's concentration allowed the endotracheal tube to catch in the bedclothes as the patient was being turned. Out it came, and since I was the nearest doctor to hand the job of putting it back in fell to me.

He was a large man with a thick, short neck, a rather small mouth and big buck teeth. I tried to force oxygen into his lungs, using a face mask, but it was no good; the air passage was blocked. I was running out of time, so I tried to reinsert the tube using a special metal instrument called a laryngoscope. It was no good, I couldn't see the right hole in the windpipe. I tried to insert it blind but it obviously went down the wrong way – down the gullet towards the stomach and not the lungs. I couldn't get the tube into the correct position. I tried and tried again, but it just wouldn't go down the right way. Starved of oxygen, the man was turning dark blue, and it would only be a matter of time before he had a cardiac arrest. It was like seeing someone fall into a river and not being able to reach them. Time was running out, and I just couldn't get it right. Already his heart-rate had slowed considerably. Here, in front of me, was a man who was about to die. In desperation I abandoned the attempt, and replaced a mask over the man's face in a desperate last attempt to blow oxygen into his lungs by hand, squeezing on a rubber bag. Around me were the nurses who had been turning the patient. They felt that it was their fault because the tube shouldn't have been allowed to fall out in the first place. Despite this, they were helping me as much as they could. I felt sick with the anguish, because my inability to replace that tube had turned what should have been a simple incident quickly rectified into a full-scale emergency. All of us knew that the heart would stop within the next few seconds.

Eventually a senior registrar arrived. He had taken only a few minutes to get there, but it had seemed like an eternity. With his skill, the tube went back into place very easily, and once his oxygen supply had been re-established, his heart rate began to pick up. Soon it began to race as oxygenated blood once more surged through the coronary arteries. His colour changed from deathly grey to healthy pink. I looked anxiously at the patient's pupils, and they both reacted briskly to light. The patient went on to make a full recovery. Although he had saved the day, the senior registrar's obvious skill simply highlighted my own woeful inadequacies. It had been a very close shave, and was a lesson I didn't forget. There is no spur to learning and improving basic medical techniques in Intensive Care quite like seeing someone almost die simply because of a lack of them. Years have now passed since that day, but I have no difficulty in recalling every single moment, even now.

Fundamental aspects of Intensive Care that are virtually taken for granted by senior doctors on a unit are often the cause of great worry and fear among junior doctors during their first few weeks on attachment. For instance, one of the dangers of putting a patient with diseased lungs on to a ventilator is that the pressure of air blown into the lungs by the machine will burst that part of the lung which is the most weak. It's rather like putting too much air into a bicycle inner tube which has a weak wall. It's called a tension pneumothorax, and anyone who has spent a reasonable amount of time on an Intensive Care Unit knows to look out for it. As a junior doctor, I knew the theory of this condition, but had never come across it in real life. That was just about to change.

Connecting a patient to a ventilator requires a lot of concentration. There are so many things to get right – the correct volume of air delivered by the machine, at the right frequency and pressures, and the correct settings on each dial. The machines used in Intensive Care can appear frighteningly complex, especially when you are unfamiliar with a particular model. For an experienced junior doctor it is an arduous task, and when the final checks have been made, there is a natural tendency to relax. That's exactly when a tension pneumothorax occurs, just when you are least prepared for it.

My first-ever case in Intensive Care was a man with bronchitis. He had been a heavy smoker who had now contracted a chest infection and he needed ventilation to tide him over until his health improved and he regained enough strength to breathe on his own. It was in the middle of the night, and just as I had finished connecting him up to the ventilator, it suddenly happened.

A tension pneumothorax can easily kill a patient. Air passes out of the punctured lung into the surrounding chest cavity. Pressure builds up quickly and strangles the heart, and not enough oxygen is getting through to the blood. There is an imminent danger of cardiac arrest. The patient goes blue, and his blood pressure drops rapidly. The remedy is to drive a large needle into the chest, allowing the air trapped in the chest cavity to escape. If you're lucky, you will have about two minutes to decide what to do. But this isn't as easy as it sounds. All of these symptoms can also be caused by a number of other conditions, unrelated to tension pneumothorax, in which case, plunging a needle into the chest of a seriously ill patient for the wrong reason isn't going to do them much good. Ironically, it may cause the very problem you are trying to solve.

There was no time to take an X-ray or to call in the boss. Action had to be taken immediately. I was fairly new to the Unit and hadn't had time to build up a close working relationship with the nurses. Standing there by the bedside, with the needle in my hand a question went through my mind: 'Am I doing the right thing here?'

'Yes,' I thought, 'I think I am . . . probably'. So I plunged the needle into his chest – and there it was, the reassuring hiss of escaping air. I had been right, I had done it. Nowadays, I wouldn't think twice about ramming a needle into a patient's chest on such an occasion, but that was my very first time. It was a satisfying moment, and it was obvious to everyone that I had done the right thing. I felt that the nursing staff had confidence in what I was doing after that. I remember feeling that I had passed their test, which as a junior doctor is very important. The man recovered, and later was well enough to return to a general ward.

It was a happy ending to a situation where I had been fortunate enough to have been proved right. During my career in Intensive Care I have been lucky enough to have chosen the right course of action more often than not. However, not all of the cases I have treated have been concluded in such an ideal manner. It is a strange trait of human nature that I often have to think very hard indeed to remember any one of the large number of cases where I was able to reach a correct diagnosis under pressure and select a treatment which undoubtedly saved a patient's life, but I do have to try very hard to forget the handful of cases where I was wrong, and as a result of my failure, the patient paid the price.

One such patient hadn't been breathing well for a long time and high levels of carbon dioxide had built up in his bloodstream when, as a junior doctor on the Unit, I put him on to a ventilator. I was surely doing the right thing. The ventilator would certainly improve the amount of oxygen his lungs were able to absorb, and would soon help remove the carbon dioxide that had built up to dangerous levels. Shortly after I had connected him to the machine, his blood pressure sank like a stone, and he had a cardiac arrest.

My mind was working furiously. Why is this happening? What the hell is going on? What should I do now? The sister passed me, reached for the defibrillator and gave him shock after shock of high voltage electricity to kick-start his heart back to life. Each time there was the familiar click and whine as it was charged up. Each time a warning was shouted 'Clear the bed!' followed by the dull thud as the shock passed through the chest. Then there was an anxious examination of the electrocardiograph trace while it settled from the shock – waiting to see a return of electrical activity. Each time there was nothing. His pupils had become unresponsive to light. We had been trying to resuscitate him for twenty minutes to no avail. He had been a heavy smoker and had severe coronary disease and chronic bronchitis. The time had come to accept defeat and abandon further attempts at re-suscitation. In the midst of feverish activity to save his life, he slipped away.

Again, I wondered why his blood pressure had suddenly fallen. Was it anything I had done, was there something I had missed? No, there was nothing I could think of. It was just one of those things. Patients on Intensive Care Units are all very seriously ill, and seriously ill people tend to die. That's all there was to it, and in that vein, I went to see the relatives, and explained to them what had happened. I said I had tried to save his life but nothing had worked; despite all our best efforts, he had died. It was just one of those things. They thanked me profusely, and said that they were sure I had done all that I possibly could under the circumstances. They knew that he had been given the very best of care.

Only afterwards did I find out the truth. Discussing the case the next morning with my boss, she mentioned that I shouldn't feel too bad about the man's death. It was an accepted risk in such cases, but in future, I should remember to introduce ventilation a little more cautiously. As she continued to speak, I suddenly began to realise that the man's death had not been the random incident I previously believed. Slowly, the full story began to emerge: I began to fear I'd caused that man's death.

His heart had responded to the high carbon dioxide in his blood by increasing the flow of blood around the body. The presence of the carbon dioxide was acting as a stimulant to his heart, thus increasing his blood pressure. When I put him on a ventilator, and quickly removed the carbon dioxide, that stimulus went with it, and I hadn't given the patient extra fluid or stimulant drugs to make up the earlier deficit.

That patient died because of my inexperience. For days I thought about it. If only I had known about this hidden complication before starting to ventilate the patient, he would still be alive. It sapped my confidence, and for a long time afterwards I lived in fear of coming across another illness that I didn't know enough about. Only after a few more successful diagnoses was I able to resume even a semblance of my previous composure. Later on, I began to accept that this risk, this uncertainty and the danger of placing the patient in peril through inevitable ignorance, goes with the job. Yet I cursed myself and felt guilty and somehow wished that I could make amends.

That was over fifteen years ago, and I occasionally think about it still. I'm sure that my experience is not exceptional. I believe that any Intensive Care doctor in the country, and perhaps most of those in other areas of medicine could recall an almost identical horror story of their own.

CHAPTER SIX

Nurses

SHE HAD BEEN ATTACKED with a shotgun as she lay sleeping in her bed, and by the time we saw her, most of her face had gone. For days she lay in a coma unaware that her husband had been killed as he lay beside her or that her children had been left alone, safe but terrified in what must have been a house of unimaginable horror. When she regained consciousness, the police guard wouldn't let us tell her what had happened; they wanted to be sure that whatever she said later would be her own words, rather than a reflection of any suggestion from us. Neither was anyone from the family allowed in to see her. As far as she was concerned, one minute she had been sleeping in her bed, and the next she was awake with horrific injuries in a strange room, surrounded by strange people.

The tube carrying air into her lungs prevented her from speaking, so the policeman handed her a pad and a pen. 'Tell us who did this to you,' he said, and told her to write down everything she knew.

At first, she was confused, and page after page of the pad filled up with squiggles and illegible marks and crosses. Then slowly, her writing began to take shape, letters slowly becoming clear, and then entire words in a shaky hand which grasped the pen as if her life depended upon it. Making an obvious effort, she placed the pen to the paper, concentrated on moving her hand, and wrote slowly and deliberately on the pad. When she had finished, she looked up, and nodded her head to the policeman. The nurses, eager to know who had done such a terrible thing to this poor woman, looked across to the policeman, waiting to hear what she had written. He looked at the paper, and then up at the nurses in surprise.

114

Across an entire page, she had written: 'They did it. Keep them away from me,' with a large arrow pointing towards the two nurses who had tended and cared for her twenty-four hours a day, for the previous three days.

A slap in the face for a difficult job well done is nothing new to the nurses on the Intensive Care Unit, but this was a particularly hard slap. Together with the doctors, they had worked so hard to keep this woman alive, and now it was obvious that she was frightened of them, and genuinely believed that they were responsible for the attack. Knowing that shock, disorientation and the residual effects of the sedatives were to blame for her confused state was no consolation when they could see the terror in her eyes as they approached the bed. She even flinched when they touched her. For six long days they nursed that woman, constantly reassuring her that everything was all right, before she was well enough to be transferred to another ward. Later the police made them sign every page that the woman had written, even the pages of squiggles, as proof that she had indeed been the author.

I have a great admiration for the nurses who work on the Intensive Care Unit – both male and female. A patient's life here will often depend more upon a nurse's skills than those of the doctor. A nurse never leaves the patient's side – and that is what separates this Unit from all of the other wards in the hospital. Every patient here has at least one nurse with them every minute of the day, twenty-four hours a day for the entire duration of their stay. This concentrated care provided by our staff is what really gives us the ability to look after critically ill people.

Most of the patients who come here can breathe only with the help of a machine. They are heavily sedated, completely helpless, and depend entirely upon our nurses to do everything for them – all the small details of care and movement which conscious people take for granted.

As you read this book, try to count how many times you have blinked your eyelids, or shifted into a more comfortable sitting position, or crossed and uncrossed your legs? How many times have you moved your tongue around the inside of your mouth, or moved your fingers or even made something to eat? How many times have your turned your head, moved a leg, or decided to go to the toilet? These are just some of the tiny actions which we give little thought to but are an essential part of our waking lives.

Most of our patients can't do any of these things for themselves. They can't move their eyelids, so if the nurse doesn't keep them moist, the eyes will become red and painful and may develop an infection. They can't move their tongue to distribute the natural secretion of saliva around their mouth, and deprived of this natural movement, the mouth becomes the source of an infection which may spread to their lungs, endangering their lives. They depend entirely upon a nurse to clean their teeth, suck out any excess secretions and disinfect their gums. So deeply unconscious are many of our patients that even a simple action such as opening the fingers of a closed hand cannot be done by themselves. They depend upon a nurse to gently straighten each finger into a more comfortable position. The patient can't speak, and so is unable to tell the nurse what they want her to do. It is up to the nurse to use her intelligence to spot the long list of small things which will make that person comfortable. It is almost impossible to imagine the infinite attention to tiny details which is everyday practice on every Intensive Care Unit across the country.

A nursing care plan for each patient is drawn up at the start of the day when the early shift arrive. It is based on a very detailed assessment of the patient and takes into account the events of the previous day. The plan will dictate how they are to be looked after, and all the various procedures which have been tailored to that individual case for the next twenty-four hours. At the end of each shift there is a careful reassessment to ensure that the planned care has been effective, and if necessary the plan is changed and updated. Many of the staff who work here are vastly experienced, and may want to suggest small changes in treatment to take into account a patient's progress across the duration of a nursing shift. The doctors on this Unit are always ready to listen – usually they are right!

Patients who come to this Unit are critically ill, and sometimes at the point of death. They need the greatest concentration of care during the first few hours of their stay, as we struggle to stabilise their condition. It isn't unusual to see one patient surrounded by two doctors and three nurses, each working feverishly with a specific job to do. Time is of the essence, and what happens in the next few hours, or even minutes, will dictate whether that person lives or dies.

Intensive Care nurses are a doctor's eyes and ears on the unit.

Constantly by their patient's side, monitoring every development, they are able to give the most accurate assessment of their condition. We depend upon them to notice and record all aspects of the patient's physiological state. They are trained to detect even the very small details which may reveal how their condition is about to change. Visitors to the Unit may sometimes see them perched at a table and stool at the end of each bed, writing down long lists of measurements into large charts, rather like Victorian ledger clerks. These figures enable the medical team to plot a patient's progress over a twenty-four hour period, so that we can see an overall trend to their illness and alter the treatment accordingly. Such trends are often much more revealing than an examination at one point in time.

It's a very demanding job, bearing little resemblance to nursing on a general hospital ward. Here, each nurse has only one patient to look after, but since they are responsible for every aspect of that person's welfare, the workload is enormous. I suppose on occasions it comes close to being on a flight deck of a jumbo jet coming in to land at Heathrow. On this Unit, there are three nursing shifts every day, each about eight hours long. Patients who are very ill are seldom in a stable condition. They can deteriorate extremely rapidly, so if a nurse isn't aware of exactly what is wrong with her patient and his present condition, right from the minute their shift begins, the results can be fatal. There often isn't time to take leisurely decisions. Nor does the patient often get a second chance if you take the wrong one. Sheer professionalism is the only way to operate, so at the start of each shift, the nurse who is taking over will discuss the patient in great detail with the colleague she is about to relieve. She will need to know about any changes in the patient's condition which have occurred during the previous few hours. They will go through the patient's main body systems, one by one, describing how well the kidneys are working, the heart, lungs, the gut, and discussing any injuries the patient may have. Next they discuss the treatment the patient is being given, what drugs must be administered and how often, and any possible complications which might set in.

It's an exhaustive process which is designed to equip the oncoming nurse with the information necessary to do all the right things in the few vital minutes available in an emergency and to detect any significant change in a patient's condition. It also means that the care we provide for each patient can run seamlessly around the clock, twenty-four hours a day without any part of it altering in any way. This important chat is called the hand-over. No nursing shift on Intensive Care ever begins without it.

At the start of each shift, every nurse will assess their patient, quite literally from head to foot so that they can detect even the most minor problem.

Patients with head injuries are in constant danger that the brain, like any bruised tissue, may swell rapidly, causing yet more damage. Measuring the pressure inside the brain is only one in a long list of observations each Intensive Care nurse has to make every hour. By each bed is at least one monitor, a screen traversed by different coloured wavy lines, each providing us with a different piece of information. One shows the jagged trace, the electrical signal from the beating heart, a straight line broken by two opposing peaks, surely the very symbol of life.

It reveals the heart's health – its rhythm – and is the line most closely scrutinised by relatives keeping watch by a critically ill patient's bed. Other lines display the blood pressure in the arteries and central veins. A small clip on the patient's finger or toe measures the amount of oxygen being carried by the blood simply by analysing its colour. The more red the blood, the richer it is in oxygen. The more oxygen in the blood, the better it is serving the tissue of vital organs which will determine whether a patient lives or dies. Some of the data is continuously fed into a computer at the patient's bedside, where further information is calculated and constantly updated.

Reading figures from a machine sounds simple, but nurses must have the skill to know when to believe those measurements and when to suspect that the measurement may be incorrect. Tiny tubes floating inside the patient's body may become blocked and pressure sensors can move and give false readings. The machine may not be calibrated properly. It may be incorrectly assembled, so that what looks like a safe reading is masking the fact that something is seriously wrong. No matter how sophisticated the machine or how powerful the computer, if a rubbish reading goes in, then a rubbish conclusion comes out – our machines are all only as good as the staff who use them. There are an enormous number of reasons why readings given by machines can be wrong, and our nurses have to know them all. A person's life may depend upon it.

The ventilator is the most commonly used machine on the unit, and like many specialists, the nurses on this Unit can tell when it isn't working properly just by the sound. Should one fail to work, the patient is deprived of oxygen and may die within three minutes. The nurse must make sure that the right volume of air is going into her patient's lungs at the right rate at the right pressure with the right amount of oxygen added to it. Modern ventilators are very sophisticated computer controlled devices with many controls to be mastered.

The nurse has the job of spotting first any change in these readings, any indication that the patient might be reacting adversely to any treatment or procedure.

They will check the patient's eyes, recording the pupil size and reaction to light, vital indications of brain activity, as well as making sure they are moist, and bathing them with fluid poured on to a small pad over each eyeball if necessary. Gluey secretions in the patient's chest have to be sucked out regularly, sometimes every few minutes. The volume and character of such secretions may indicate the onset of a chest infection and must be recorded carefully. The volume of the stomach's contents is measured, bowel sounds are a good indication of how the patient's gut is working, and whether they are able to digest food – a vital requirement before attempting to feed them by stomach tube. Otherwise, the nurse will be expected to supervise a drip feed into a vein. Every hour the urine volume is measured, an important indication of how the kidneys are working. Every hour all these observations are carefully recorded on the chart.

In addition to keeping a medical watch over the patient they will have to care for them as well. They wash an unconscious patient's hair, often using their favourite shampoo exactly as if they could do it for themselves. They clean their teeth, shave the men, and keep all of the patients as tidy and neat as possible. Some patients have chronic diarrhoea, and need to be changed every hour. It is the nurse's duty to make sure they are lying in a comfortable position. They have a total responsibility to care for each patient as they themselves would want to be cared for.

Relatives will see this as a sign that their loved one is being looked after to the best of our ability. It's an enormous work load requiring a lot of training and experience to get all the tasks done in time. I know I couldn't do it.

There is another important subject that the two nurses will discuss during the hand-over, which has little bearing upon the medical care of the patient, but which is vital nevertheless. It's a delicate matter, but one which is characteristic of being a nurse on an Intensive Care Unit: they will discuss the patient's relatives, and how they are coping with the strain and sense of helplessness of seeing a person they love critically ill and perhaps near death.

Many of the relatives sitting alongside that patient will be distraught and barely able to speak. Others will want to talk constantly about the life they have shared with the patient in better times. All will need an understanding and sympathetic approach from the nurse. Knowing who each relative is and how they are reacting is essential at the start of a nursing shift if a nurse is to care for the relatives as well as the patient.

The nurse is a constant attendant and may be assigned to the same patient for the entire duration of their stay. In effect, they become an adopted part of the patient's family, privy to every discussion held by that bedside, no matter how intimate, no matter how revealing. It's a privileged position, demanding sensitivity and diplomacy. It is a task which often cannot be performed without a great deal of courage as well as medical knowledge. Many of the scenes which our nurses have to witness are harrowing in the extreme. Every patient has a story to be told, and every death is a tragedy. But some are even more tragic that others.

One mother of a nineteen-year-old girl was holding her hand as she died and asking the nurse; 'Who am I going to read poetry to now that my daughter is dead? Who am I going to talk to, and share all my secrets with?' And she told the story of how the young girl had been difficult in her early years: how she had been involved in drugs and gone out with boys of whom her mother didn't approve; how she had changed, and after years spent in quarrels and bitterness, the two had become close again. She was the prodigal daughter returned to the fold. The teenage rebel had turned into a friend.

Now she was gone. Her mother had no one else at home and would have to face life on her own. You could see her thinking about those years of arguments and the harsh words that had been said, and how she wished that things had been different. And how, for a moment, in her mind's eye, her daughter was not dead, but young and alive again, dressed in toddler's clothes and then in her first school uniform. A lifetime of memories, like pictures on a page, flashing across her thoughts, as she sat by the bed, still holding her daughter's hand. The nurse stayed on to comfort the mother as she had done for each eight-hour shift, every day for the past five days.

As the patient lies unconscious it is natural for the relatives to include the nurse in every conversation. They hear the circumstances which brought the patient to our unit, about his family and how he has a sense of humour. How he likes to play golf, or which football club he supports, and how all the neighbours send their best wishes. They see the relatives' hopes rise, and hear their plans for the future and how they are going to celebrate when their loved one is well enough to leave hospital. And surely that won't be long?

Often it is a lesson in optimism fulfilled – but sometimes it is a study of despair at close quarters. They hear the words of guilt, the muttered pleas for forgiveness, and see faith crumble bit by bit, until the bitter end. And then they see the tears and hear the sobs of utter despair.

The nurse's job is to support the relatives as much as – and sometimes even more than – the patient. It is not unusual to see a nurse with her arms around the shoulders of a relative who is crying her eyes out because a loved one has just died. Nor is it unusual to see that nurse with a tear in her eye too, showing that she cares.

As a doctor, I can avoid most of these scenes. Often, I will simply move on to the next patient, and use my professional detachment to distance myself from what I have just witnessed. I can simply think of other things or go to the coffee room for a break and a chance to talk things through with colleagues – but the nurse has to stay. Sometimes, the strain is so great that they will ask another nurse to take over for a few minutes while they go for a break, but often it can only be a temporary respite. Is it any wonder that nurses who work in Intensive Care have a special quality all of their own?

Although mercifully few, inevitably some of the scenes that occur here are too much to bear, and nurses have their breaking point just like anyone else. Often it may be because they have been nursing a young patient who has struggled to stay alive only to deteriorate to a point where we have been forced to withdraw further treatment. After perhaps weeks of caring for that young person, the nurse is suddenly expected to give up.

It is even more upsetting when a patient has been well enough to speak, and the nurses have got to know them well through conversation and shared jokes. They look to be well on the way to recovery – before suffering a relapse which eventually kills them. Those conversations will have broken down the nurse's defence mechanisms, so that the patient has already become a friend by the time they die. Yet there is nothing that can be done to save them.

Some of the most difficult cases to nurse are those where you can imagine a member of your own family or someone that you care for dearly in the same situation. No matter how hard you try, you can't help but see the face of the person you love in that patient's place.

One nurse had to look after a patient dying from cancer when her own mother had died from exactly the same disease just two weeks earlier. She hadn't told anyone, thinking that she could cope, and so had tried to carry on. But as the disease progressed, she increasingly began to think of her own mother, and how she had suffered too. Finally, she couldn't take any more and broke down in tears.

It's very difficult to cope with these emotions, and I have no doubt that for many nurses who are committed to the job, the death of a patient is as much a bereavement for them as it is for any of the relatives. What makes matter worse is the reaction of some relatives when their loved one has died – it is not uncommon for relatives to behave in an unpredictable way. They will have been under pressure for weeks, and this tension always has to find an expression somewhere. Perhaps they feel that they have somehow contributed to a loved one coming to Intensive Care in the first place.

Sometimes they will shout and swear and hurl abuse in sheer rage and frustration at what they regard as the unfairness of death, the sheer cruelty of losing someone they loved, and the person who is often the target for their anger is the nurse. They accuse them of not doing everything you could, of negligence and disinterest in the patient. They shout at them just for being there. We know they don't mean it, that it's just their way of showing how much that person meant. Not every nurse on this Unit has had this experience and it's a deeply unpleasant one at the time.

Strangely, there seems to be a correlation between the most

abusive relatives and those who later send in the nicest letter of thanks after the patient has died. It's as if they are trying to say: 'Please forgive us, we know that you did your best, and we're sorry for what happened.'

An unconscious patient is a very difficult patient to nurse. Without speech, and with most of their face hidden, it is very difficult to give the patient a personality. They can't tell you what they do for a living, or the hobbies they have or where they live, or whether they are married with a family. They can't make jokes, or say what they thought of the programmes on television last night. All the nurse can see is a body, attached to a variety of machines, and perhaps the only signs of life may be the trace of the heartbeat on a monitor and the warmth of the patient's skin. This can go on for days or even weeks and perhaps the patient may never recover consciousness until they have recovered sufficiently to be moved to a general ward. Or else they may simply never recover consciousness at all. Despite the lack of response, the nurses always talk to the patient, because they can never be sure how much or how little the patient is aware of what is happening. For instance, they will always tell an unconscious patient what they are going to do before touching them on the assumption that no one would want to be suddenly moved around without being asked first.

Like all of the staff on Intensive Care, the nurses give their patients a character they have invented themselves. A patient's notes may list his wife as the next of kin, so using that information, the nurse imagines him as a family man, with a house and a car, and perhaps a dog; they imagine him going to work – perhaps he is an office worker, or a car mechanic, or a plumber – and they imagine him going to the pub with his friends, and doing all the things that the nurses themselves may do in their daily lives. I do the same thing myself, and it is interesting to compare the personality that you invented for the patient with the real thing on the occasions when they return to the unit to say thank you.

Inevitably there is the occasional nurse who cannot handle the daily emotional drain of working on the Intensive Care Unit. After a while, they become tearful, and take periods of sick leave which become longer and longer as the strains increases, until they reach a point where they cannot face going back to work.

Eventually, they will be interviewed by the senior nursing manager because of their sickness record, and after much support and full discussion, may decide that working on Intensive Care is no longer for them.

This has happened to some of our best nursing staff, and there is no shame to be felt under these circumstances. The very thing which makes them such good nurses in the first place, also leaves them open to the crippling effects of stress: they are warmhearted people, who care deeply for their patients but who now can no longer cope with the strain of watching those people die.

Some come to this conclusion themselves, and decide to move on without anyone ever realising that they have been feeling the pressure. Others need a gentle conversation with close colleagues who may have noticed changes in their behaviour before the full story emerges. I know of nurses who have left the Unit and gone to work in other areas of the hospital, or even left hospital work altogether, ostensibly because they wanted a career change, but really because they wanted out.

Strangely enough, however, we don't lose many nurses through stress. This is probably because each nurse is carefully selected before coming to work on the unit and the ability to withstand stress is one of the important criteria. There is also an element of self-selection, and nurses generally won't apply for places on the unit unless they know they can cope with the work.

Everyone works together as part of a close team and there is a lot of support provided by friends and colleagues on an individual basis. Times for 'letting off steam' are essential. There are frequent opportunities in the form of curry evenings, pub crawls, stag nights, hen nights, and a host of other occasions that are probably best forgotten.

Although they are very strong individuals, nurses who work on Intensive Care tend to share a common characteristic. All of them want to work in a unit which demands a very high standard of nursing care. Each has found the experience of working on general wards frustrating because of the corner cutting which is inevitable when looking after a greater number of patients.

They find it very frustrating to offer anything less than perfection, and enjoy being stretched professionally. Intensive Care gives them the time and the resources to do just that. They know that a doctor's decisions on what treatment to give will often depend upon what the nurse has said. Many thrive under the pressure, and the 'adrenalin drive'. They see themselves as the patient's advocate and have no hesitation in fighting to make sure their patients get the best possible treatment. They operate as part of a team which goes hand in hand with the doctor's approach to patient care. In many cases, the more senior nurses will have a far better knowledge of the specifics of Intensive Care than a junior doctor arriving for his first stint on the Unit.

To be a nurse on Intensive Care, you must first qualify as a general nurse, and then have about a year's experience of working on some other ward before even being considered for the job. Next come the interviews which select the most suitable individuals for such a demanding job. Sometimes, I sit in on the interviews for the more senior posts and am always impressed by the thoroughness of the selection procedure. My nursing colleagues are extremely good at seeing who will make the grade and who won't. They can spot those who won't stand emotional pressure, or won't be able to cope with difficult relatives or be able to work with colleagues as part of a team. All of the nurses here face continual pressure throughout the entire shift, so any successful candidate has to be good at organising their work and managing their time. They must able to organise their tasks, the treatment, and perhaps the most important of all, they must be able to organise the doctors, probably the toughest job of the lot.

At first they receive one month's supervised training on the unit, introducing them to common working practices, the special techniques employed to nurse seriously ill people, and all of the specialised equipment – the ventilators, monitors, haemo-filtration, suction, blood gas measuring machine, temperature control devices, and even the special beds which prevent patients from suffering pressure sores. It takes a comparatively long time before they become an operational nurse on the unit, simply because there is ample opportunity to get things wrong, and the cost of a mistake can be very high. It is so easy to do dangerous things on an Intensive Care Unit without realising it; in some instances even moving a patient can cause a drop in their blood pressure, with possibly fatal results, so every nurse has to know what they are doing. To become a fully trained Intensive Care nurse they take a special six-month course organised by the English National Board. It is extremely hard work, and nurses can only qualify when they have proved themselves adept in all aspects of Intensive Care. For those who qualify it means that doctors can rely on their judgement and they have the respect of their fellow professionals in the Unit. They are extremely bright, highly motivated people, many of whom will decide to go further still by studying for degrees and even postgraduate courses such as the diploma in critical care nursing. It is a sad fact but there is no doubt that in this country the nursing profession has got its act together far better than doctors when it comes to training in Intensive Care. We work as a team, and nursing here is a speciality in its own right.

The very skills which make them special also mean that they are very difficult to replace. Staff illness or a sudden emergency where we need more nurses can pose terrible problems. It's no good just taking a nurse from a general ward or a nursing agency and plonking them into the middle of an Intensive Care Unit. An untrained nurse requires supervision, occupying still more of the other staff's time so even with the best will in the world, they would be worse than useless. At first sight, the number of nurses on the Intensive Care Unit would seem to be a dull logistical problem, of little concern to an outsider. But if we don't have enough nurses to assign one to each patient, it can mean the difference between life and death. The best medical techniques and the most sophisticated equipment in the world are only ever as good as the people who use them.

On this Unit, we depend primarily upon the dedication of the nurses who work here to plug the inevitable gaps which occur in staff ranks and no one minds too much if they are phoned at home and asked to come in, or alter their shift patterns at very short notice. Even though it may mean cancelling a social engagement, or changing their plans, few of the nurses will refuse because they know the consequences for the patients if they don't come in. I realise that this is exploiting their consciences, but sometimes there is no alternative, and the nurses who work here understand that.

However, this method can only be used for very short periods, perhaps three or four days at a time. Nurses who work long hours soon become very tired, and therefore a danger to the patient. We also risk losing their good will, which is perhaps the most vital commodity on the Unit.

So, we try to plug the gaps in other ways as well. Many of the nurses who leave the Unit do so to get married. Working full-time on an Intensive Care Unit is not completely incompatible with family life, but it can make things very difficult. Rather than see the skills of highly trained people go entirely to waste, we have developed a bank of ex-Intensive Care nurses who are willing to work part-time at very short notice. Many of them have been trained on this Unit, and I know most of them personally from the days when they worked here full-time. They are invaluable, and have helped us to keep the Unit working to full capacity many times.

Techniques in caring for critically ill people are changing all of the time, however, and the only real way to keep abreast of modern methods is to work regularly in an Intensive Care Unit where they are being applied. Even the best-trained nurse can feel rusty and out of step with the Unit after a few months' absence. Those who stay away even longer sometimes lose their confidence completely and are afraid ever to return. We need to work out a method of in-service training for part-time staff, so that they are able to keep their skills finely honed. After all, it would be a good investment, producing a fully flexible, fully trained reserve of nurses for comparatively little outlay. I believe that it is time to tackle some of the hidden hurdles which prevent trained staff from applying for part-time work. For instance, it might be cost effective to spend money on child care so that In-tensive Care nurses with children could be freed from their domestic commitments at short notice. As always, the argument comes down to economics and the merits of an invisible gain against a very visible outlay.

Surveys show that relatives often have a much better rapport with the nurses on Intensive Care than they ever do with the doctors, even though in theory the doctor is in charge. Nurses often have better communication skills, will answer questions more freely and in a clearer manner and show more care for the relatives than their medical colleagues. Doctors are often very bad at breaking bad news to relatives and giving up necessary time that this important task requires. It is not uncommon for them to put the boot in and then walk away, leaving the nurses to stay there and pick up the pieces. The very title 'Doctor' can often make you seem unapproachable to ordinary people, while the nurse is seen as more equal. The bedside nurse has often built up a strong relationship with her patient's family. Under these circumstances, it is inevitable that the nurse becomes the strongest advocate for a patient's welfare, insisting that they receive the best treatment and sometimes challenging the doctor's views.

Accepting such challenges, and having nurses question your professional judgement can be a very constructive experience. It helps me to clarify my own thoughts. It keeps me on my toes, and I know that it is done for the best possible reasons by people I respect. The nurse is usually in a much better position to ask these questions than anyone else, and they have a right to know the thinking behind every decision, because they, in turn, will have to explain that decision to the relatives. They are playing a very important role as intermediary, bringing a more human touch to what can appear to be a dispassionate clinical puzzle. Although I can see little but benefit, I also have to admit that such relentless, and sometimes aggressive interrogation, is not to every doctor's taste; some find it very threatening.

The nurse's role becomes particularly clear when medical treatment is failing and their patient looks likely to die. They are quick to let you know when they think treatment should be withdrawn, and from my experience, more often than not they are right. However, like all particular points of view, that opinion has to be seen in context.

I remember one nurse, looking after a particularly arduous patient, who argued quite fervently that the case was hopeless, and instead of continuing treatment, it would be much kinder to let him die. She had been looking after a young boy with multiple injuries, and I knew that she had children at home who were roughly the same age. She was a very experienced, reliable nurse, yet we couldn't agree to let him die. It was clear to all of us that this was an inappropriate view to hold. There were quite clearly very good medical reasons for continuing the boy's treatment, reasons that she herself would normally have said were grounds for optimism. As she continued to speak, her distress became obvious and the full story began to emerge. Looking after the young boy had been so distressing that the strain had overcome her mechanism for coping with the case. All she could see was her own son, and she was overwhelmed by the thought that plagues us all: that there, but for the grace of God go I. She could see her own son lying on the bed, and couldn't bear the thought of him suffering or being in pain. When she argued that the boy should be allowed to die, what she had really meant was that she could not longer stand the pressure of nursing him. She wanted out of the situation, but couldn't bring herself to recognise it.

After the discussion, some of her colleagues took her aside, to let her talk through her thoughts and work out the emotional turmoil that had been building up inside. She was moved to a less-onerous patient for a few shifts, giving her time to come to terms with the things she had seen. Soon she was back to her old self again. The decision to continue proved correct and after a long struggle the young boy was discharged from the Unit, well on the way to recovery. Such cases don't happen that often, but when they do, the nurses recognise it themselves, and deal with in their own way.

No one could do this job unless they could see very good reasons for wanting to endure the emotional lows. For every tale of gloom, there are three success stories, and this is the compensating factor which carries all of the staff here over the bad patches. Feeling that you have played a part in saving a person's life is one of the most satisfying emotions in the world.

While outsiders concentrate on the gloom and doom of the job, nurses often tell me about some of the unexpected pleasures. One such story involved a young lad in his early twenties who had been brought into Intensive Care from accident and emergency. He had been involved in a very nasty car crash. His vehicle had smashed into a tree, flinging him through the window. He came to us with severe head injuries, and unable to breathe. A ventilator was keeping him alive while we waited anxiously to see if there was going to be an improvement in his condition.

The true extent of permanent damage caused by head injuries is always very difficult to assess. While the patient remains on the ventilator, they must be sedated, and only after these powerful drugs have been withdrawn is it possible to get any real measurement of how badly the brain has been injured. Weaning the patient off a ventilator is, therefore, a moment of truth. Only then does it become clear whether the patient will be able to make a full recovery, or as is more often the case, has suffered various degrees of permanent disability.

Fortunately, this young man began to recover, the sedative

drugs were withdrawn and soon he had reached the point where we felt he was strong enough to breathe for himself. It was then time for him to come off the ventilator. As the lad began to re-gain consciousness, the nurses withdrew the endotracheal tube which had carried the ventilator air into his lungs. Normally, such patients simply doze, taking their time to come round fully, so the wait to see the true extent of injury is prolonged even further. However, this young man must have felt us all hoping and praying that the permanent brain damage wouldn't be too bad. Rising to the occasion, he suddenly sat bolt upright in bed and shouted: 'Where the fuck am I?'

As his nurse was later to say: 'Those were the sweetest words I had ever heard.' They meant that, despite all the odds, he still had the ability to speak clearly and logically. With a performance like that, there was no doubt that this young fellow was well on his way to making a full recovery. He left the Unit a few days later, and is now, I believe, back at work.

Many of the patients who come to us are some of the most seriously ill people in the region. Patients who are on the road to recovery sometimes find it difficult to cope with being sur-rounded by people who are so desperately ill, and may sometimes slip into a state of despondency.

Sometimes, unorthodox tactics have to be used to give them a badly needed boost to their morale; something to give them an incentive to recover, a reminder that there are very important reasons for wanting to get better.

One of our patients, a middle-aged man in his mid-fifties, had been crushed during an industrial accident at a factory. Although very ill when he came to us, he had made good progress, and was now almost ready to leave the Unit to return to a general ward. However, his breathing still wasn't quite strong enough. We noticed that his rate of progress had slowed in direct propor-tion to an ever-increasing gloominess he seemed to feel for the future. He certainly needed something to cheer him up – and that's when the nurse noticed something unusual about his bed.

Many relatives bring in photographs of the patient's family, friends, or favourite places they have been. The snapshots are usually stuck on tracking above the bed so that the patient can see them when lying down.

This man too had several photographs stuck to the rail above his head, but looking at them, the nurse realised that they all showed the same thing. There wasn't a single photograph of his wife, or any of his three children; every snapshot was a different picture of his dog.

He loved that black-and-white collie. According to his wife, his dog always came first – before her, before his family, and even before his drinking mates. And that's when the nurse knew exactly what to do. Next day she helped the man into a wheel-chair complete with mini oxygen tank, and said: 'I've got a surprise for you.' Wrapped up well and with porters standing by should anything go wrong, he was wheeled downstairs, and out into the car park. Waiting there, by the corner of the building, was his wife. When the nurse gave the signal, she disappeared for a moment – and then reappeared seconds later, accompanied by the same black-and-white collie which had featured so promi-nently in his pictures.

The dog rushed up to greet him, and the man was overcome with the emotion of it all. This is what he had wanted, but lately he had begun to think that he would never see his dog again.

It was only a very short reunion but it made all the difference. Cheered up, he continued to improve, and soon was well enough to leave the unit for a general ward.

CHAPTER SEVEN

Human Cost

THERE IS MEDICAL EQUIPMENT worth hundreds of thousands of pounds on this Intensive Care Unit. Ventilators cost at least £20,000 each, and the plethora of syringe pumps, haemo-filtration machines and portable mini-laboratories aren't far behind. Even the beds here can cost a small fortune. Yet the item most frequently used to bring comfort to countless number of people costs little more than a tenner. It's the electric kettle to be found in the staff rest room – for it is here, over a cup of coffee or tea, that we all let off steam.

No one can do this job for long without coming across a case which breaks their heart. We all try to remain detached, to see each person as simply another patient lying on the bed in front of us, someone who needs to be treated dispassionately to the best of our abilities. Becoming involved isn't necessarily a good thing. Everyone will have their own individual defence mechanisms to save them from the full horror of some of the things they have to witness.

Doctors have an easier time than nurses because we don't have to stay by the bedside every moment of the day. When confronted by a heart-rending scene, we can retreat to the medical details, the facts and figures which enable us to plan our treatment, rather than dwell on the patient's personal circumstances. We can always move on to the next patient, losing ourselves in the next case, rather than think about the one we have just seen. Or we can bury ourselves in some administrative task. Yet for most of us there are times when we drop our guard and are caught unawares. It's at times like these that we head for the staff room and the electric kettle.

Here there is no hierarchy between doctor and nurse. We share

132

our experiences and feelings with each other. Talking about what happened and how we feel is vital if we are to come to terms with harsh facts. We have to come to terms with an average of one hundred and sixty failures each year, and break the news to one hundred and sixty families. Tears are never seen as a sign of weakness. Rather, they are a sign that you trust your colleagues to such an extent that you aren't embarrassed to let them see that you, too, have feelings.

Tears can burst out at the least expected moment. One patient, who suffered a serious head injury while on holiday, was cared for by the same nurse, every day, for all of the three weeks of his stay. He was about the same age as the nurse's own husband, his wife was the same age as the nurse herself, and their child was also, by cruel chance, the same age as the nurse's own child. The parallels between the patient lying unconscious on the bed and the nurse's own life were immense, and so she formed a bond with the family. When the patient died, she too felt a sense of bereavement, but like the professional she is, carried on with her work, putting the needs of the relatives first, comforting his wife and child.

I was in my office later that day when she knocked on the door, and asked to speak to me. At first it seemed like she wanted to have a general chat about work on the Unit, but suddenly she burst into tears and the whole story emerged. I wasn't surprised, for hers had been a very stressful case to manage.

I put my arm around her to comfort her. I didn't say anything, but simply listened as she told me about the stress she had been under, and how she had tried to reason it away herself, but couldn't. Slowly, she began to feel better, and apologised for being foolish. There was no need, because we have all been in a similar situation ourselves at some time.

At moments like these, just as you are innocently sitting with your arm around a nurse, you know that some strange force will bring someone barging through the doors. To anyone outside the unit, it must appear a compromising scene, and probably does wonders for my reputation. However, the staff on this unit know exactly what the score is. That day it was the nurse who needed to be comforted. Later it might well be me.

In my free time, I like to pursue sports and hobbies which demand total concentration, so that there is no time to consider any other aspect of my life other than what I am doing at that particular moment. My colleagues are the same. One loves to roar around the countryside on a powerful motorcycle, or play Bob Dylan songs badly on his electric guitar. But for me, relaxation comes from hang-gliding or mountaineering.

Climbing is especially relaxing. As well as the physical exertion, there is an intellectual component. It's a bit like chess, having to work out not just the next move, but the move after that too. You get to see the world from high places – and nature at its best. I went climbing in Scotland in winter recently; the sky was a brilliant blue, and all around me was fluted ice, sparkling like crystal in the slanting light of the morning sun.

There is a camaraderie between climbers, a very intense friendship between people who find themselves in a dangerous situation where you think you all might die together, sharing the hazards, or sheltering in a storm tent on the side of a big mountain for several days. I get frightened like anyone else, but I quite like being in a dangerous situation and being in control. Climbing up a steep ice gully, feeling the adrenalin surge and looking at the scenery around me. I feel the joy of being alive.

My main sport now is hang-gliding. I've always wanted to be able to fly – the sensation of zooming off into the blue yonder is a tremendous feeling of freedom. I'm alone and able to soar, dive and turn as I see fit, with just one fragile wing holding me aloft from the earth. Once again, I can feel the thrill of being alive, of having one life and being able to make the most of it. Feeling the wind in my face, and seeing the light spill across the countryside as I fly above it with only the quiet rush of wind in the wires is my idea of living life to the full.

Feeling the emotional stress of work is perhaps the most obvious personal cost paid by all of the staff who work in an Intensive Care Unit. Unfortunately, there are other, much worse prices to be paid in your home life and by those who you love the most.

As consultants in Intensive Care we work an average of seventy hours a week. A typical day begins at 8.30am, and doesn't finish until 7.30pm at the earliest and much later when we're on call frequently right through the night. As well as our clinical work there's all the day to day administration, so there may be endless meetings and paperwork. Nor does work end when we finally go home. The junior doctors on the Unit fare little better. Although welcome legislation has now limited their hospital hours to fifty-six hours a week, they now work a shift system and must spend long hours outside work preparing for rigorous postgraduate specialist exams.

It's an enormous amount of time to take out of family life, and few people can sustain it without suffering the consequences. Doctors in general, but Intensive Care specialists in particular, have a far higher rate of divorce, suicide, alcohol dependency and family breakdown than the average population. Three out of the five consultants on this Unit have suffered the collapse of a marriage.

We don't have to look very far to see why our marriages fail. Often dinner might be waiting at home, but we are still stuck on the unit, overseeing the treatment of a patient who had just been admitted, or talking to relatives who could only come in after their work had finished. Perhaps our children are waiting up especially to say good night to the dad they seldom see, but still he doesn't arrive home on time. Then there are the countless number of sports days, teacher–parent evenings and other special occasions where we have to phone up at the last minutes to say: 'Sorry, I'm tied up at work. You'll have to go without me.'

When we do come home, often after a particularly hard case, we tend to feel physically and emotionally drained. All we want to do is sit in front of the television, regardless of what is on, with a can of cold beer, unwilling to speak or be sociable until we have been able to relax on our own for half an hour. Ironically, this is just the time that our families wanted to talk to us most.

Work makes us unreliable. At the start, it may be a bit of a joke, and our families expect us to arrive an hour after everyone else. But as the years pass, with no change in sight, the joke begins to wear thin. Tempers flare at the prospect of yet another evening ruined; it becomes easy to assume that we are simply wriggling out of family responsibilities. Weekends are not much better. A week on call sees us away from home, and working through one weekend leaves us exhausted for most of the best part of the one that follows.

A successful family life demands a certain degree of commitment – to routines, to spending time with your children and perhaps the most easily forgotten of all, to each other. Often we can't give our families what they need the most. We can't give them more of our time. Slowly at first, but with ever gathering speed our families learn how to live their lives without us.

There is a moral pressure which prevents the partners of people who work on an Intensive Care Unit from raising too much of a fuss when the job always comes first. Office workers who continually stay late can easily be criticised for giving up too many of their evenings to do work which could quite easily be done the next day. The common cry from a wife to her husband who has spent the entire weekend filing spreadsheets is: 'It's hardly a matter of life and death.' However, in our job, it may be precisely that.

Partners rightly feel irritated because work is occupying too much of your time, and complain that it is being done at their expense as well as your own, yet, at the same time, they feel guilty, because the sacrifice is being made for a just cause. They feel it is impossible to shout at you for coming home late when the reason for your delay is that you have been trying to help a seriously ill human being to recover. In the beginning, this serves as a gag to what should have been a normal argument. But as time goes on, that feeling of guilt in itself becomes a source of resentment.

Some say that it is possible for a wife or husband to become used to having this way of life foisted upon them. They say that the best thing to do is to marry someone within the profession, someone who therefore knows and understands the demands that this job makes upon your life. Statistics show this is not true. No matter how understanding my wife was at the start of our marriage, the fact that we cannot take part in the practicalities of family life became impossible to tolerate. In the end, it becomes too much to bear.

Like most of my colleagues I have considered taking another job outside Intensive Care, which would enable me to earn a comfortable living and give me a normal life at home. The new job would give me more free time to spend with my family, time that I could use to see my three young children growing up. There would be no doubt that home life would be easier and much more fulfilling and that I could begin to pursue all of my other interests free from the pressure of life on the Unit. It seemed a natural and perfectly easy escape route. But I didn't take it. I didn't even bother to fill out the forms. I knew that it wasn't for me.

All of us have made a conscious decision a long time ago that we want to work on an Intensive Care Unit. We have shaped every step of our careers, moving from department to department and hospital to hospital, to learn the skills that every good Intensive Care specialist must have to successfully treat patients who are close to death. We enjoy the direct nature of life on the Unit. Infusing a drug into a patient's veins, I can see the effects straight away. We can see if our treatment is working or not, using the information supplied by monitors and charts measuring vital signs of the body's physiological function. Giving people a few pills and telling them to come back to see you in a week's time doesn't hold the same attraction. We enjoy the camaraderie of the staff on the unit, the closeness, the feeling of working as a team, the absolute requirement to act quickly and decisively, the satisfaction of carrying out a practical procedure quickly and effectively, and the contentment of seeing inexperienced junior doctors become confident and competent practitioners in this new and exciting medical speciality.

I couldn't walk away from all of that. Now, I have made my choice, or at least, I have come to accept the consequences. Fortunately, so far none of my children wants to follow in my footsteps. My eldest son is torn between being a geologist studying earthquakes or a marine biologist studying sharks in the South Pacific. Both are far more sensible options!

Chapter Eight

A Lighter Side

THE CAR CRASH HAD BEEN A BAD ONE and the young lad was in a terrible state. Cuts covered his body, bones had been broken by the force of the impact, but most worrying of all was the head injury. It looked very serious, and already his brain was beginning to swell dangerously as he was admitted from accident and emergency to the Intensive Care Unit.

The treatment given to a seriously ill patient during the first hour after their accident is probably the most important of all. This time is known as the Golden Hour, for swift skilful medical care given as soon as possible after the event can often prevent further complications which would ultimately cause the patient's death. The lad was in a horrendous condition, and things were not looking good. Time was of the essence, because what happened over the next few minutes would have a major impact on whether he lived or died. He had been transferred straight up from Casualty. Each member of the team knew their job and were following a well-rehearsed procedure, rather like a crew in a grand prix. They had done this many times before. As the tension grew, no one was saying very much as each struggled to insert tubes, ventilate with oxygen, set up drips, put the monitoring probes into place, and keep a record of his heart rate and blood pressure. He was bleeding internally; bags of blood were being squeezed into his veins as fast as they could manage. Each bag had to be carefully checked to ensure it was meant for him and not someone else.

And that's when it happened. One of the nurses, who had been reading the crossmatch form to check his name, date of birth, and blood group, suddenly shouted out: 'Hey, today is his birthday!' Sure enough, hastily scribbled down by the admitting doctor in casualty, was his date of birth showing that the young lad lying battered, bruised, and fighting for his life on the bed in front of them was indeed twenty-one years old that day.

What cruel twist of fate had brought him to Intensive Care on this of all days? He should have been out dancing or down the pub with his friends enjoying himself. Under the circumstances, there was only one thing to do. Hearing the news, the entire team immediately took a deep breath, and sang a very quick but tuneful verse of *Happy Birthday To You*. The patient was unconscious and didn't hear a thing, but the song had broken the tension, and after a quick cheer, it was back to work. Anyone watching would have been appalled, and wondered what kind of people can sing and laugh while treating such a seriously ill patient? But thanks to that team's hard work and skill, the lad recovered. Because of them, he is still alive and able to make it a birthday to remember.

I can imagine the words of the song ringing out from behind curtains closed around the bed, while everyone else was wondering what the hell was going on?

There is a tremendous sense of community on this unit. The people who work here are a very tightly knit bunch, despite the wide range of characters who do the job. Everyone knows everyone else extremely well: we know about each other's home life, families, husbands, wives, boyfriends, girlfriends and the present state of their relationships. A close bond exists between the staff who work here and they have more in common with each other than with other nurses and doctors in the rest of the hospital. They work hard and play hard together, as anyone who has ever been to our social outings or Christmas parties can verify. They know how to let their hair down, and on these occasions, rank has no value.

The nurses who work on this Intensive Care Unit are not angels, nor are the doctors paragons of virtue. They are merely ordinary people working in sometimes extraordinary circumstances. We all have good days and bad days – days when we are irritable and short-tempered with each other, days when nothing seems to go right no matter how hard we try. Few people on this unit bear any resemblance to the self-sacrificing characters who seem to populate health service soap operas on television. Instead, the staff on this Unit have quirky natures as well as notable qualities, which means that some of the things that happen on this unit will seldom appear in a television writer's script.

One aspect of my work that I never see reflected in the hospital dramas is the endless flood of quite disgusting and often hilariously funny instances of black humour. Even in the most tragic circumstances, you can be certain that someone will make an utterly tasteless remark which will reduce the place to hysterical laughter. It's an odd facet of human nature which urges us to laugh defiantly in the face of overwhelming horror. Injury and death in particular seem to evoke a peculiar desire to crack a joke or two.

There are jokes common to all Intensive Care Units in hospitals across the country. All of them are particularly cruel and quite inappropriate for the occasion, but somehow you can't stop yourself from smiling either through shock or genuine amusement.

One of my colleagues was the consultant in charge of the Unit during a particularly bad period when we had to withdraw treatment from several patients in a matter of days. It was just his hard luck to have a run of patients so severely ill that further treatment was pointless. When deaths occur in a spate like that, it can have a profound effect upon the morale of doctors and nurses alike, whatever their experience. At the end of his period in charge of the Unit, it was clear to everyone that my colleague had had enough.

Helpful and sympathetic as ever, some of the nurses here decided to give him a boost. In tribute to the depressing ordeal that he had just been through, and as a show of solidarity and support for his actions, they gave him the cruel nickname 'The Terminator'. It has stuck ever since.

I'm not sure that all the remarks we make are entirely funny, in fact many are quite disgusting and in very poor taste, but it's part of the culture of the place. Every hospital I have ever worked at has been exactly the same. People who have to deal with sights which are so shocking that they would make the average man on the street freeze in revulsion and panic, seem to use tasteless remarks to release tension which would otherwise prevent them from doing their work well.

Some of the cases seen on the Unit can be very difficult to keep in perspective. Looking around, you can see nurses and doctors struggling to ignore the relentless horror by injecting a little bit of unreality into the situation. It's their way of lightening the load, because they know that later, sitting at home on their own, they will think about that case for days after the event.

One young boy was admitted to the Unit after he had been trapped under some falling scaffolding. The force of the blow had knocked him to the ground, and the metal tubes had crushed his abdomen and broken his back and severed an arm. It was a tragic case which upset us all, and an air of gloom descended upon the team who had been treating him as they took a break. From the severity of his injuries it was quite clear that this boy would never lead a normal existence again. As is usual in such cases, everyone in the coffee room was thinking of how they would react should such a catastrophe happen to one of their own children. Even in theory, it wasn't a prospect we could bear pondering.

We all knew what sort of future he faced. When other teen-agers were out enjoying themselves, in clubs or dancing in discos, he would be severely disabled, unable to do many of the things his friends took for granted, and forever seen as 'that poor boy'. Instead of a youth full of carefree fun and laughter, he would be confined to a wheelchair for the rest of his life. It was an unbearable thought, and one which stunned us into silence. And that's when someone added: 'Even worse, with only one arm, he'll end up going round in circles'.

From the outside, it appears odd that anyone should want to say these things at a time when the patient they are treating may be fighting for their life. It may also seem a very disrespectful way to behave, and not the sort of thing the public expects from its nurses and doctors. I often wonder why we turn to such sick humour. Perhaps it is for the following reason.

Place anyone in any of the circumstances that the doctors and nurses on this Unit have to face every day, and their first human instinct is to be frightened and upset. Seeing someone die before your very eyes in no joke, no matter how many times you may have seen it before. All of the staff here feel a sense of bereave-ment themselves when a patient dies, and it can be a crippling influence if you let that feeling get to you. So humour, even black humour, is part of the defence mechanism. It alters an un-pleasant experience, making it that little bit less threatening, that little bit more removed from stark reality to something that is slightly absurd. It's the staff's way of saying: 'I'm not upset by this situation. I'm in control. See, I can even make a joke about it.'

It's a way of coping. A lot of the best people I have ever worked with in Intensive Care also seem to be those who had the vilest form of humour. As long as it doesn't get out of hand by being said in the presence of patients or relatives, or anyone else other than staff, humour is an invaluable device for breaking down the tension created by a particularly bad case.

Humour also tends to rear its head at the most unlikely times and in the most unexpected ways. One of the worst duties on this unit is breaking the bad news to the relatives of patients who are going to die. It's a task which requires preparation and sensitivity, and every doctor has to have time to work out exactly what they are going to say before walking into the interview and beginning to speak. It's a very serious undertaking, because your words will have an enormous effect on that person, and you're only going to have one crack at it. Unfortunately, the Unit is often so busy that there is little time to work out in advance what you are going to say, so you trust your experience and innate sense of tact and diplomacy. Usually, it's enough to get by, because none of us find it hard to imagine what it would be like if we were the relative waiting to be told bad news, so we treat the family and friends of our patients as we would like to be treated ourselves. But even with the best intentions, words sometimes let us down.

One of my consultant colleagues remembers with horror the time when, as a junior doctor, he first had to break bad tidings to relatives. The family were assembled in the waiting room to hear news of their father, but it wasn't good. The poor man didn't have much longer to live. They had all been waiting expectantly for some time. The job should have been done by one of the senior consultants, but for some reason, he wasn't available, so the sister grabbed my colleague and marched him down to see the relatives. No one had ever taught him what to do or what to say, nor did he know fully the details of the case, but there was no one else around so he just had to get on with it.

Sitting down he could see that the family was deeply upset, so speaking in a gentle tone, he very carefully went through their father's symptoms, and told them why there was no longer any hope. Everything went very well, and they were very pleased that he had taken the time and trouble to explain so carefully what had happened. My colleague was feeling very pleased with himself at having handled a difficult situation with such aplomb and sensitivity, and was just getting up to leave when one of the relatives asked the most difficult question to answer: 'How long do you think he has, doctor?'

Even for a doctor who knows the fine details of a case, this is a particularly difficult question to answer correctly. There are few cases when you can predict with any certainty exactly when a patient will die, and any attempt to be precise invariably ends in disaster. If you plump for a short time and the patient lives far beyond that, it calls your entire medical judgement into question, so that relatives begin to doubt the skills of the doctor who was looking after their loved one. Plump for a long time, and if the patient dies quickly, the relatives may not have had time to prepare themselves, having believed that the patient would linger on. The art of answering this question is to be imprecise. But that knowledge only comes with experience. Desperately wracking his brain to think of an answer, with no details of the case to fall back upon, for the first time his composure cracked, and for some strange reason which he still doesn't understand he found himself blurting out the single word 'six'. Nothing else. No other phrase, no other sound, except 'six'. It was an answer worthy of Confucius, so obscure and open to interpretation that even modern art critics would hesitate to be so beguilingly brief.

'I didn't know what I meant by "six"', he explains, 'and I'm sure that the relatives knew even less than me. It could have been six minutes, six hours, six days, six weeks or even six months. It just seemed like a sensible figure to say. They looked a bit puzzled, and for a moment there was a silence, and then they said, 'Fine doctor. Thank you very much,' and seemed very pleased with the answer.'

Sometimes, when telling relatives bad news, it is worth remembering that their agenda may be different from yours, so that the reaction you get may not be what you expect under the circumstances. It was precisely that breakdown in communication which lead my same colleague into difficulties when dealing with the family of another of his patients.

He was a working-class man in his mid-sixties who had smoked a lot, and so no one was surprised to find that he had very bad lung disease. Smoking had also diminished his circulation in general, seriously reducing the blood supply and leaving surgeons no option but to amputate the affected limb. My colleague had admitted him to the Intensive Care Unit after the surgery because he was making a very slow recovery from the anaesthetic. After only a few days his condition deteriorated still further, and gradually became worse and worse. He had a large family, with quite a few kids, so it wasn't going to be easy to break the bad news to the family, but it needed to be done, things were looking bleak. To soften the blow, one morning he spoke to the man's wife and prepared her for the worst, which he felt certain would not be long in coming.

The next day, sure enough the poor man had deteriorated still further and the decision was made to let the patient die in peace. Now it was time to speak to his family again. The children were upset, but his wife took it surprisingly cheerfully. My colleague went through the details of her husband's case, explaining what had happened, what had been done and why we couldn't continue. She seemed satisfied with that, and the conversation was coming to a close when she put her hand into her purse, pulled out a form and handed it to him. 'Would you mind filling that in for me doctor?' she said.

He looked at the form. It took him a little while to work out what it was, but then it finally sank in. It was an application form for a transfer from her high-rise flat to a council owned three-bedroomed bungalow. Nottingham City Council, like most other councils in Britain, has a long waiting list for council homes. One of the longest waiting lists of all is for three-bedroomed bungalows; would-be tenants have to demonstrate exceptional circumstances before even being considered for these homes. One such reason is poor health, and sure enough, as the woman very kindly pointed out, this was a section which had to be filled in by a doctor.

It was an unusual way to react to news that your husband was shortly going to die. So unusual that my colleague came to the conclusion that the woman's grief may have clouded his attempts to explain the gloomy outlook. 'I'm sorry,' he said, 'but perhaps I haven't made myself clear. I'm afraid your husband isn't going to get better. He's not going to need a council bungalow. Unfortunately your husband is going to die.'

Her reply stunned him. She said, 'I know that. But his breathing is bad at the moment isn't it?' There was certainly no denying that. The man was receiving 100 per cent oxygen as it was, and even so, the amount of oxygen in his bloodstream was falling. 'And he wouldn't be able to walk upstairs since he only has one leg, isn't that right?' she continued.

Yes, that was also certainly true.

'Well then, if you put that down on the form and send it off to the council before he dies,' she said, 'I won't tell them when he does die. And then I can have the council bungalow.'

He didn't know what to say. He could barely believe what he was hearing. Often, he had seen people in tears in this room – indeed, he had almost come to expect that reaction – and yet here was a woman talking about council bungalows just minutes after hearing that her husband was going to die.

Finally, using his typical diplomacy he said, 'Perhaps we ought to leave it for a while and see what happens.'

Upon leaving the room, his immediate reaction was: 'What a selfish attitude.' Later, however, he began to see the logic behind the woman's suggestion. It wasn't going to make any difference to her husband whether she applied for the bungalow or not. She was approximately sixty-five years old and had obviously been desperate for a council bungalow for years and years, and perhaps saw this as her last chance. Maybe having that bungalow would have been her only compensation for losing her husband. What harm would it have done? He began to feel the heel for having refused to play ball. The woman's husband died later that night, before someone with a stronger claim could be robbed of a bungalow.

Dealing with the occasional horrific sight in Intensive Care could in theory, make you into a much harder person. Sometimes that does happen, and I know some who have become battle weary, worn down by yet another tragic story, and eventually defeated by one teenage death too many.

Although a somewhat macabre humour is part of the culture of every Intensive Care Unit, there is a golden rule and that is that you don't crack jokes when relatives are around or whenever a patient might be upset by the remark. Sometimes, the occasional burst of laughter at the top of the Unit carries across the beds to a seriously ill patient whose relatives know he is going to die. It seems a totally inappropriate sound for such a sombre occasion, and I often expect the relatives to complain. Much to my surprise very few ever do. Instead, in a strange way, the laughter is often taken as a very reassuring sign that no matter how grim present circumstances seem, life will go on, and someday, those same relatives will be laughing again too.

145

The best smiles are the ones you get from the people who come to the Unit seriously ill and then get better. It's a different sort of smile than the humour but it's nicer by far. One young lad in his late teens came to us after a head-on smash with another car on the road between Nottingham and Leicester. By rights he should have been killed, but his life was saved by a doctor who saw the accident happen, and stopped to lend a hand. Only his skill at resuscitation had enabled the lad to survive long enough to get to hospital, and despite emergency neurosurgery to remove a blood clot from the vein, things weren't looking good. When he came to the Intensive Care Unit from theatre, his pupils were fully dilated and fixed, which is usually a very bad sign. He wasn't moving after the accident and it became clear to us that the lad had a horrific brain injury and it would probably only be a matter of time before he became brain stem dead and lost all of the remaining reflexes that he had. We didn't hold out much hope, so that when his father came in to see him, we tried to prepare him for the worst.

Much to our surprise, far from dying, twenty-four hours later the lad showed a slight improvement. One of his pupils began to respond to light from a torch, constricting in response to the light. It was the first indication of control of bodily movement by his brain that we had seen since his admission. Then, hours later, the other pupils too began to respond to light, but instead of feeling joy, I felt utterly gloomy. He wasn't going to die, but on the other hand, the quality of his life would be so horrific as to be beyond comprehension. He would probably remain in a persistent vegetative state, alive but almost in a permanent coma. Even if his condition did improve, the most his father could hope for was a teenage son who was profoundly handicapped, totally dependent on full-time nursing care, a boy who would always be a burden to his family right up until the day he died.

He continued to make slow improvement, and despite all my misgivings, eventually recovered sufficiently to be moved out of the Intensive Care Unit and back on to a neurosurgical ward. I remember talking to his father shortly before the move, and feeling very sorry for him. Here, surely, was a man whose dreams and hopes for his boy had been shattered.

I lost touch with the lad after he left the Unit, and I assumed that he would be looked after in a nursing home for the rest of his days.

For many years I have been interested in the outcome of patients with head injuries who have been treated on the Unit. We regularly hold a clinic where our old patients are invited to come back in for a follow-up examination so that we can see how they have progressed, and what skills if any have returned with the passing years. We always contact their General Practitioner first just to check that they are still alive, and then invite both the patient and their carer – usually a relative – to come along. It can be a depressing business, because often the patient has progressed little since leaving hospital, their recovery reaching a plateau after a few years, with any further improvement restricted to small steps rather than giant leaps.

I invite their carers too, because the brain damaged patient often doesn't realise that they are handicapped in any way. Ask them how they are and they might say: 'I'm fine thanks,' and they will genuinely mean it. Often only the person looking after them will know how badly they have been affected, and so are able to provide an accurate assessment of the patient's progress. When I saw the lad's name on the notes, I remembered the case quite clearly, and also the severity of his injuries. I looked at the entries I had made at the time of his crash, recording his lack of response to stimulus, and the slowness of his recovery, and I prepared myself to see a dribbling young man, unable to speak more than a few words and certainly confined to a wheelchair and I wondered how his father and mother were coping with what must surely have been a colossal strain.

There was a knock on the door, and I looked up to find him standing there, smiling, looking fit and healthy just like any other lad in his early twenties. As I stood up, he walked across the room and shook my hand. I couldn't hide my disbelief; I was shocked, and he could see it. So too could his dad, and both of them grinned from ear to ear, because they knew what I was thinking. How on earth had he managed to recover to such an extent? I had expected him to die, or at the very least to be, quite bluntly, a mere shell of a human being. How on earth had he done it ?

To compound my amazement, it turned out that the lad was about to go to college to study for a degree in Business Studies. Yes, he had some residual difficulties, but none that would slow him down substantially. He didn't remember anything about his stay on Intensive Care, so I spoke to his father and reminded him of the bleak hopes for recovery that I had held for his son when he first came on to the Unit. He remembered those dark days perfectly, and now here he was, showing his son off with pride.

I derived immense pleasure from that meeting, and the effects lasted for days. It was a tremendous feeling, for here was living proof that all of our efforts had not been in vain, even though we had held out little hope of such an outcome. I think it's great when patient's cock a snoot at the medical establishment – it's great when doctors are wrong. We tend to be a bit self-important, and live in a world where we think we can predict how these things are going to go. It does us good when things turn out differently.

CHAPTER NINE

New Life

LISTENING TO THE LOUDSPEAKER on the monitor, you could hear the tiny baby's heart beating rhythmically inside the womb – even though its mother was now brain dead. A little mite, just twenty-eight weeks old and no heavier than a bag of sugar, struggling for life in the midst of death. For the time being a machine would keep air flowing through its mother's lungs. Drugs would support her blood pressure, maintaining the blood flow to the placenta providing the oxygen and nutrients which the unborn babe needed to survive, but soon, we would have to act.

For five days we had tried to save the mother's life. She was just twenty-five years old and looking forward to the birth of this, her first child, when a blood vessel burst inside her head. It was one of those random events, something no one could have predicted, a result of a natural weakness in the vessel wall which strikes without warning but with catastrophic results. One moment, she had been leading a normal life, perhaps chatting to her husband or friends, and the next, as the vessel burst, she had collapsed in a coma. Robbed of oxygen by the sudden haemorrhage, her brain stem had eventually died, and now there was nothing more we could do.

Her husband was shattered. The couple, recently married, had been on the threshold of a bright new life together, and were looking forward to all the joys that family life can bring. Now that dream was over. It had ended here, on the Intensive Care Unit, where the young woman now lay, surrounded by medical equipment and monitors, none of which could now save her life. And yet, those same machines were also the source of new hope, because there, amidst all the usual Intensive Care paraphernalia

149

was the special baby doppler monitor signalling the insistent squelch, squelch, squelch of the unborn baby's heart battling to survive.

Usually in such circumstances, the baby doesn't live long. They either miscarry, or die in the uterus, unable to overcome the trauma suffered by their mother. Yet this little character seemed to be making a go of it. Ultrasound scans showed it sitting happily in the womb, and despite all the drugs we had given the mother in our attempt to keep her alive, so far the baby's heart-rate and blood flow seemed normal. As well as the Intensive Care nurse monitoring the mother's condition, a midwife visited regularly, watching for the slightest signs of foetal distress, until we were ready to carry out a caesarean section. At twenty-eight weeks, the tiny baby would be painfully premature, barely able to cope on its own, with the odds for life stacked heavily against it, yet we couldn't keep its mother going for much longer. It wasn't an ideal way to be born, but at least the baby would have a chance to survive.

And survive it did. It was very weak, very small, and spent a long time in a neonatal Intensive Care unit, but it did live. Here was a child who by rights should be dead, but one that had been saved by good fortune and modern medical techniques. Even though its mother had died before it was born, that little baby was destined for a future on this earth.

For a long time afterwards, I wondered how that woman's husband must have felt later as he held the tiny baby, barely bigger than the size of his own hand, and experienced the unparalleled emotion of seeing for the first time his own flesh and blood. What must it have been like to savour the joy of a newborn child, the sense and certainty of life continuing, but all the while knowing that its mother, his wife, had just died. It should have been a joy shared by two, yet there he stood, surrounded by people but undeniably alone.

By now, that child is probably another face among a crowd of tiny faces at a local primary school, running and laughing and doing all the things that bring pleasure to parents the world over. Nothing will set it apart, or ever suggest that it has entered this world through troubled times, but I have no doubt that on that little face, relatives and friends will often be able to see a look, a smile, or an expression which they will instantly recognise as having once belonged to the mother it never knew.

Intensive Care has acquired a reputation in the public's mind because many of the people who come here are about to die. I prefer to think of it as a place where people are brought to be given a chance to live. Usually we think only of those of our patients who did not die, and recovered to lead normal lives having benefitted from this chance. However, there are many others who may be given a chance to live as a result of actions taken by the Intensive Care team, even though we may never meet them. Some of our patients who die can give the chance of life to others.

The donation of human organs from patients who have died here has meant a new life for countless numbers of people across the length and breadth of Britain. Deciding to donate the organ of a loved one is one of the most difficult but generous acts that a relative can perform. In the midst of sorrow, it is a decision that cannot be delayed to allow grief to subside, and one which requires a great deal of courage. Yet I am always surprised by the number of people who, just moments after being told that a loved one has died, agree that the patient's organs should be removed to benefit complete strangers who are still alive. Out of all the other units in this hospital, the Intensive Care Unit provides by far the greatest number of organ donors. Only a narrow band of people are suitable as potential donors, those who have died whilst attached to a ventilator, whose heart continues to beat maintaining their vital organs in perfect health. Every organ that is except one, the brain, that has become irredeemably injured so that the patient exists in a state of irreversible unconsciousness. The state of brain stem death. And because of the treatment we are able to provide, most of them come to this Unit.

In general, the most common organ donor will be between nineteen and thirty-five years old, in previous good health but killed by head injuries or brain haemorrhages which will have left the rest of their body perfectly intact. This hospital has a specialist neurosurgical unit, which treats people from all over the South Trent region, so we see more than our fair share of patients with these types of injury. All will have died on the Unit despite every attempt to save their lives. Only after all hope has gone and the diagnosis is certain are they ever considered as potential organ donors.

This is an important point, because I want to stress that we put the welfare of the patient first every time. No one is ever admitted to this Unit unless we feel we have a chance of making them better, and our first and only task at that stage is to save that person's life. Despite recent criticism, there is absolutely no question of a fatally injured person being taken on to the Unit with the intention of keeping them alive long enough to get their organs. Only after it has become quite clear that we have lost the battle to save that life, and that as a result of their injuries the patient has become brain stem dead, do we move on to consider their potential as an organ donor. Because of the commercial profits to be made in other countries from the sale of human organs, every aspect of the procedure in this country is strictly controlled by laws and codes of practice. These take effect right from the moment we begin our tests to determine that brain stem death has actually occurred.

An old boss of mine always used to say that deciding when a patient has died is the only diagnosis that a doctor has to get absolutely right. Unlike every other condition, when an approximate answer will usually suffice, with death there is no room for even a small margin of error. The patient is either dead or they are not, and there is a substantial difference between the two states.

Determining brain stem death is not medically a difficult task, but emotionally it may be hard to believe the patient is really dead. For a start, the patient is apparently still breathing, although this is only because the ventilator is forcing artificial breaths into the lungs. The heart is still beating, pumping blood at approximately normal pressures around the body. All of the measurements on the bedside monitor appear normal. Ironically, the patient often looks an even more healthy shade of pink than usual; they have lost control over the vessels near the surface of the skin, which dilate, letting more blood through and giving the brain stem dead patient a misleadingly rosy complexion and warm feel. In fact, for every other organ in that patient's body, it's business as usual. They are receiving oxygen via the blood at the correct concentration, and having waste products taken away by the same means, so they simply get on with their work.

Yet the cells in the brain stem have died, and since this part of the brain controls every fundamental aspect of bodily function, life is impossible. In broad terms, the brain stem is the body's Clapham Junction, an area through which all of the signals to and from every part of the body has to pass. It controls all of the basic functions, such as the nerves which move your arms or legs or tell your chest to expand and take in breaths of air. In addition, it also has its own nervous system, called the Reticular Activating System, which lights up the cortex (the thinking part of the brain) a bit like switching on the electrical power to a television. When there is widespread damage to the brain stem, it's the equivalent of switching off that power, and the pictures on the screen fade to darkness. The cortex and the brain's cerebral hemispheres aren't energised, and so don't function. Nor will they ever do so again. Instead, the patient lapses into irreversible unconsciousness – by any definition, irreversible unconsciousness equals death. However, there are many complicating factors which could fool us into thinking a patient is brain stem dead when he is nothing of the sort. To make sure we get our diagnosis spot-on every time, we follow a strict procedure, laid down in 1976.

First of all, the patient must be unconscious and totally dependent upon a ventilator. The examining doctor, who must be a senior figure with expertise in this field – usually the neurosurgeon in charge of the patient or the consultant in charge of the Intensive Care Unit – has to be certain of the reason why the patient is in this condition. They must be able to diagnose conclusively some cause – usually a head injury or a brain haemorrhage – which has damaged the brain stem, and damaged it irreversibly.

The reason for this is simple. Various other conditions can cause similar temporary abnormalities, and without a positive diagnosis, a doctor can be misled into believing a patient to be brain stem dead when in fact they are very much alive. For instance, a patient who has been exposed to cold weather for some time, maybe on open moorland or in cold ocean waters would have a very low body temperature – a condition known as hypothermia. When the brain is very cold the patient can also become unconscious and show a similar degree of unresponsiveness. Drug overdoses, or large amounts of the powerful sedative drugs legitimately prescribed by doctors during previous medical treatment can have the same effect. Metabolic abnormalities and serious hormonal imbalances can also reduce the patient to an unresponsive unconscious state. But with intense treatment, most of these conditions are reversible.

To make sure that brain stem damage is irreversible, we wait for a while, and do nothing but look after the patient as we would any other, caring for their needs, and maintaining whatever care may be required to sustain life. We need to be certain that none of the brain stem cells are going to recover. Some may not be dead but lie dormant, requiring a little time before resuming normal life. Although the patient would be very severely handicapped, they would still be able to survive, and so time is allowed to pass before examining them. The exact amount of time will vary from patient to patient, depending upon the original diagnosis. Where massive brain stem damage is all too clear, it isn't necessary to wait more than a few hours, because the chances of recovery are almost non-existent. However, in cases where the brain stem has been damaged by oxygen starvation, through drowning or suffocation for instance, we have to be sure that the condition is irreversible. This may take up to three or four days.

What we are looking for is brain stem damage which is irreversible, and we can't afford to have our diagnosis clouded by additional elements. That's why, even though we may know that the patient has a severe brain injury, we examine the patient's charts, taking careful note of what drugs have been prescribed, so that we are aware of any effects they may have had. In addition, we wait for some time to let any unknown drugs – including alcohol – pass through the patient's system before conducting any formal tests to see the extent of the injury. Once we are certain that the patient's condition has been caused by injury to the brain stem, and can discount any masking effect of drugs, it is then possible to begin the definitive tests to measure the extent of that damage.

Both of the patient's pupils must be fixed and unreactive to light. These involuntary movements are controlled by the brain stem, and their absence is a major sign that severe brain stem damage has occurred. Ice cold water is poured into the patient's ear while we watch for eye movements – again an involuntary reaction whose absence is not a good sign. There should be no cranial nerve motor responses. These are the nerves which, among other things, control eye movements and some facial movements. Their presence would be a sign that part of the brain stem was functioning, giving us cause for hope that all was not lost. Finally, the patient should show no signs of being able to

154

breathe for themselves when they are disconnected from the ventilator for five whole minutes. During this time they are given oxygen, fed into their lungs by a small tube passed into the windpipe.

It's a harrowing series of tests – each simple in themselves, but mighty in their implications. As in life so in death, and there is a special form to be filled in, with a set of boxes for my signature confirming that each part of the test has been completed, and the result together with the date and the time that the tests have been carried out. After some time the whole procedure is repeated by another independent senior specialist.

Often these patients are very young, perhaps in their late teens or early twenties. They are the most physically active sector of the human population and therefore the people most likely to suffer head injuries through car crashes, fights, sport, or simple accident. Somehow, their death seems all the more cruel, because they should have had a whole lifetime ahead of them – years of being able to enjoy themselves, savouring the sweetness of youth, their days filled with sunshine and laughter. Instead, fate has brought them to this end.

No definite conclusion is reached before the second identical set of tests have been carried out later, by a separate senior doctor who must be, at the very minimum, a Senior Registrar. This ensures that such an important decision is not placed in the hands of just one doctor, who may have conducted the tests in an incorrect manner or simply failed to notice a reaction which would put an entirely different interpretation upon the findings. It's a fail-safe method of making sure we reach the right conclusion.

None of the doctors conducting the tests may be a member of the transplant team who will later remove any organ donated. The findings reached must be entirely independent of any subsequent decision about the patient's suitability as an organ donor.

Only when the second set of tests are complete, and the findings have shown exactly the same lack of response is the patient declared brain stem dead. The time of death recorded on the death certificate is the time that the second set of tests were concluded, even though the patient may have been in an identical state for the previous three days. Only after brain stem death has been confirmed may the patient be considered as a potential organ donor.

Seeing a person who is brain dead lying in a hospital bed can be an eerie experience. It defies all psychological criteria of what a dead human being should look like. Their chest still rises and falls under the influence of a ventilator, just like most of the other patients on the unit. The trace of a beating heart still moves in that characteristic peak and trough fashion across the monitor screen – to a layman's eyes, the most reassuring sight that life is still extant. The dead patient's pulse rate and blood pressure are still recorded in bright red numbers in one corner, both well within acceptable medical levels. Even the urine bag at the side of the bed fills at the same steady rate as when they were alive. It's as if death has come to visit, but left again in a hurry before making all the proper arrangements.

It's a sight I've seen more than a hundred times during my career as an Intensive Care specialist, but I can never quite get used to it. It looks as if the person is just sleeping. Logically, I know that the patient is dead, but emotionally, it can be hard to accept.

Throughout this time the patient is nursed with all the care and attention of any other patient on the Unit. The bedside nurse knows in her heart of hearts that there is no hope but must nevertheless continue to perform all the routine nursing duties necessary to maintain the patient's dignity. At the same time they must support the relatives in their grief, gradually helping them to come to terms with the appalling situation and helping them understand the bizarre nature of the condition. Many find this one of the most difficult and demanding aspects of their job.

If I can feel like that despite all my years of experience, it isn't hard to imagine how a relative must feel when asked to come to terms with the fact that this person they love is no longer alive. It's a task made easier when speaking to adults because I can explain all the medical details, all the tests and symptoms. I can speak on their level and answer their questions and help them understand how life has gone. But how do you even start to explain to a crying child that the mother they can see, and touch and feel is really dead? How do you persuade them not to believe the evidence of their own eyes?

Thankfully, this is a task I have never had to perform, because I wouldn't know where to begin. Instead, I leave that duty to relatives, letting them know that I am on hand to answer any question they may have, ready to do whatever I can to help.

One young girl was only about seventeen years old when she

suffered a massive stroke due to a blood clot in her brain. She had long auburn hair, and I remember thinking how lovely she looked, and what a tragedy this was for her parents who loved her so tenderly. It was difficult for them to comprehend how one minute, they could be sitting in their front room talking to their daughter, and the next she had collapsed into a deep coma. They couldn't accept the fact that she might not be able to speak to them ever again – there had been no warning, no time to prepare. All of us tend to imagine illness as a slow progression, a gradual getting worse, giving us time to prepare for death and say all of the things we want to say beforehand. Sometimes, it isn't like that.

At first, we weren't in a position to say whether she was going to recover or not. Brain injuries can be difficult to predict, so that a reasonably accurate diagnosis is only possible after at least forty-eight hours have passed and the brain scan has been repeated. Everybody on the Unit hoped the news would be good, but I explained the severity of the position to the relatives soon after they arrived. No one gets brought down gently by news that their daughter may well die. We all hoped there would be some signs of recovery over these next long hours but there were none.

Eventually it was time to do the tests. All sedative drugs had been stopped twenty-four hours before and she had been maintained in a stable condition throughout. I talked to her father and explained the process I was about to conduct. I told him that I was going to examine his daughter very carefully to see if there was any sign of brain activity. After the process was complete and both sets of tests were done, the answer was clear. So I went to see her mother and father again, and told them that their daughter was dead.

Immediately it was obvious that her father didn't accept it. He asked, 'How can you be so sure?' So I explained all of the tests that we had just done, why we had done them and what the result had been – but it was no good. He could only reply, 'No, no not my daughter. It's too soon. It can't be true.' And I could see the anguish of every parent who feels that nature has been turned on its head when their children die before they do. Then he asked me a question that many people in similar circumstances have asked: 'All right, even if the brain stem is dead, how do you know that the rest of the brain is dead too?'

157

Well, quite honestly, the rest of the brain isn't dead. It's irreversibly unable to function because that part of the brain which enables it to do so is dead. It was a complicated answer, and one that I knew would only make matters worse. Hearing that part of the brain was still alive had simply raised hopes that could not be realised. Sitting in that small relatives' waiting room, I could see a family searching for any straw that could help them believe that their daughter still had a chance of life. I didn't blame them. If I had been in their position, I would have done the same thing.

As her father explored every possibility, examined every nook and cranny for the merest sign of a reason to believe, it gave me no pleasure to block his every move with unavoidable fact. And as our conversation went on, it began to dawn on me that really, only one thing would help him come to terms with harsh reality. Taking a deep breath, I said, 'Would you like to see me do the tests?'

Pulling the curtains behind us we stood by his daughter's bedside, I, the father, and the Intensive Care nurse who had supported the family throughout their ordeal. The young girl probably died soon after being admitted to the Unit, but I knew that the nurse had continued to talk to her and had looked after her with the same meticulous care she would have given to any living patient.

At first I felt rather uneasy. This was the first time I had conducted these tests under such a public gaze, but I felt that once he had seen for himself that his daughter was unable to breathe for herself, it would help him accept the fact that she was dead. However, there was another aspect that worried me.

Although the brain stem is dead, it is still possible for the spinal cord to exhibit some activity. There are body movements that can occur without the signal first having to be processed by the brain stem. The knee-jerk reaction, for instance, is one such movement, and there are others. What would her father think if, on the one hand I was telling him that his daughter was dead, and at the same time he saw her limb move? I had no option but to warn him that some movement was likely, even though I knew it would be very distressing. He was an intelligent, thoughtful man and listened carefully to this explanation. I could see it made sense to him, and it was as well that I did explain this because no sooner had we begun our tests than we could see her toe beginning to twitch. I explained in detail how we could be sure that she had suffered a stroke, and how we had waited for the effects of any drug present in her body to wear off. Then lifting the young girl's eyelid, I shone a light into her eyes. The pupils didn't react, and I explained the reason why.

Much though I tried not to, in the end I had no option but to explain these techniques in detached, clinical, dispassionate terms. For me this young girl was a patient, but for him she was a daughter. Someone whom he had held in his arms as a baby, someone he had watched grow from a little girl to a young woman.

Next came the cold water into her ears, and still there was no sign of eye movement. There was no reaction to painful stimulation of the face, or any gag reflex or cough when a plastic tube was passed down her throat. I explained how there was no sign of a cranial nerve response. Then came the test of switching off the ventilator. A plastic catheter was passed down the endotracheal tube and connected to the oxygen supply. Then for five long minutes we stood in silence. There was not a sign of breath, just the rhythmical beat of the chest wall as her young healthy heart increased its activity in response to the rising level of carbon dioxide in her blood. And then, looking at me, he said: 'It's all right. I know that she is dead.' And after pausing for a moment to collect his thoughts, he walked back to his family alone. It had been a difficult time for both of us. I think he felt that it was his duty as her father to make sure that the doctors had got things right. He wanted to be sure that we weren't throwing away even a slim chance for her to live. We restarted the ventilator and oxygen was forced into her lungs once again.

But our interview wasn't at an end. There was still another topic that I had to raise and there was no option but to speak about it there and then. Could I have their permission to treat their daughter as a potential organ donor?

God knows that if I could have avoided raising the subject at that moment, then I would most surely have done so. The family was still reacting to the news of the young girl's death, and now I was about to confront them with another very difficult decision. However, it had to be done. While the young girl's body could be kept on a ventilator for many days, each passing day increased the chance of infection spreading to her organs, making them worthless to the recipient. For me those recipients weren't just statistics. Having worked with transplant surgeons in the past, and knowing people who have received organs from donors, I have seen for myself the profound difference it has made to them; in many cases it has not only changed their life, but actually saved it. These people were depending upon me – and other consultants in Intensive Care Units up and down the country – to overcome my own squeamishness and at least ask the question which could make all the difference. It had to be done.

In this country, even if a patient carries a card stating that they wish to become an organ donor, it does not replace the duty to ask relatives for their permission. They have to agree before the operation can go ahead. In some cases there may be a considerable delay while we search for next of kin, during which time there may be a deterioration in the potential donor's condition, making the organs no longer suitable.

The most commonly transplanted human organs include the heart, heart and lungs together, liver, pancreas, kidneys and corneas, but no matter which organ is involved, transplantation requires an enormous amount of preparation and organisation.

Here in Nottingham, we have a special Transplant Co-ordinator who has the job of matching the organs available from our patients to a central list of recipients. All over the country, these people are waiting for a telephone call to say that a heart or a liver of the right size and tissue type has become available, and asking them to report to their hospital right away.

She must also co-ordinate the work of the surgical team necessary to perform the operation. Often they will come from the recipient's hospital, sometimes by helicopter in the middle of the night, but at other times, we provide the surgeon and anaesthetists ourselves. She will need to know the age, sex, blood group, approximate height and weight, and chest size, as well as a brief medical history of the donor, to help her find the recipient who is best suited to the organs available. It's a difficult job which has to be done from a standing start at the drop of a hat – and it all takes time.

That is the main reason why we had to act quickly. It was essential that I summon up the courage to ask this young girl's parents for their permission within the hour, as any delay would be doing no one any favours. I asked them in my usual way, by which I mean in a slightly oblique fashion. I asked if their daughter had ever expressed any wish about donating her organs, or if she had ever discussed the matter at home, or held any views or opinions on the matter. I always ask in these terms because I feel that it is extremely unfair to ask relatives directly for their permission. It places the burden of making that decision far too heavily on their shoulders at a time when they are least able to cope. I prefer to guide them towards thinking about what the patient would have wanted had they been alive to express an opinion. I am asking them to act in accordance with what they believe would be the patient's wishes rather than taking a funda- mental decision on their behalf.

Her parents were wonderful. Despite the fact that they had only just started to come to terms with their daughter's death, they knew that this was a decision that could not be postponed. Calmly, they considered what their daughter would have wanted them to do, and after just a few minutes, they made up their minds. Yes, the young girl would have wanted to give others the chance to live, she would have wanted something good to come out of her own death.

My next question was: 'Are there any organs which you don't want us to remove?' At first glance, this sounds like an unneces- sarily macabre attention to detail, but there is a purpose. We have to be certain that relatives understand exactly what we are pro- posing to do to the body of the person they loved. Relatives will often give permission for surgeons to remove every organ which can be transplanted – all except one. They don't want the eyes of the person they loved to be touched.

Whenever we think of anyone's face, and the spirit which lies within, we automatically think of their eyes. Whenever we speak to people, face to face, we look at their eyes to see what they are really thinking. The old saying is that the eyes are the windows to the soul; they light up everyone's face, and sparkle with humour, or shine with anger. This thought passed through my mind as I asked this question.

Few relatives can stand the thought of the eyes being cut out, even when it is explained that the surgeon will carefully fill the space and close the lids so that it will look as if the body is asleep. The heart, pancreas, and kidneys are merely parts of the body which no one ever sees, and even with the best intention in the world, it is difficult to summon up the memory of a loved one simply by thinking of their liver – but the eyes are a different matter. They have personality.

The young girl's parents however, gave me their permission to remove every organ that could be usefully transplanted. It was an extremely brave decision, an incredible act of compassion and I knew that it could mean a new quality of life for up to six people. Two patients suffering the endless misery of dialysis would receive one kidney each – that's all any of us needs to do the job properly. Someone with a diseased heart, tottering on the brink of death but clinging to the hope that somehow a new heart could be found in time to save their life, would now have that hope fulfilled. Another person with chronic lung problems would now have the chance to lead a normal active life. Perhaps another young girl of a similar age lying in another Intensive Care Unit whose liver had been destroyed by a paracetamol overdose would be given a chance of life. And thanks to that couple's courage in the midst of tragedy, a person robbed of their eyesight would now have the opportunity to see the wealth of colours and wonders of the world, perhaps for the first time.

Now it was time for them to say goodbye to their daughter, and I knew that it was better for them to be left alone. As they stepped behind the curtains surrounding the young girl's bed, only the Intensive Care nurse remained, monitoring the patient's heartbeat, and making sure that she remained in a stable condition while trying to be as unobtrusive as possible and fight back her own tears as the family sobbed with grief. Already preparations for the surgery which would remove the girl's organs were well under way, and soon a theatre assistant would arrive to wheel the girl's body to the operating table where this last procedure – which we call 'harvesting' the organs – would begin.

Some relatives prefer to accompany the patient right to the theatre doors, and wait for them outside until surgery is over. Most, however, say their last farewells there at the bedside.

On this Unit, about 25 per cent of the seriously ill people we admit every year do not survive. This means that in a small area with just twelve beds, we have an average of about 165 deaths of every kind. However, the actual number of people who subsequently donate any of their organs is comparatively quite small, no more than twenty people per year. There are various reasons for this, but the most common cause is that the patient who died was not suitable as a donor because of the illness which killed them. Transplanted organs must be perfect in every way, so that anyone who has suffered chronic illness is automatically ruled out.

Tissue testing reveals the presence of any harmful bacteria or viruses. The person receiving the organ will have had their immune system artificially disabled by drugs to encourage their body to accept the new organ as its own, and will therefore be unable to fight off a new infection. We especially check for the presence of Hepatitis B and HIV, diseases which would certainly kill a healthy person, never mind someone in the recipient's condition.

When everyone is ready the donor is moved to the operating theatre. The donor is given an anaesthetic and kept on a ventilator just like any other patient undergoing surgery. Muscle relaxing drugs are also given, as well as drugs and fluids to keep the blood pressure normal, and antibiotics to keep bacterial infection to minimum, but the donor is not alive. They are dead, but since their heart is beating, they have not yet become a corpse. Junior staff, seeing this process for the first time, often find it very distressing, but I've seen it too many times not to have fully worked out my moral stance on the matter: I view it as a process which will extend life for others. Perhaps one of the greatest acts of kindness one human being can make to another. Something worthwhile and positive coming out of a situation of utter waste.

The heart is stopped by injecting a cold solution through the vessels. Slowly, the organs are cut away from the surrounding tissue and harvested. All are stored in sterile bags, and surrounded by ice in special containers for the journey to their new owner. Then, and only then, the ventilator is switched off for the final time. Some people might view this as the ultimate moment of death, but in reality, it has taken place a long time before. The patient's wound is carefully sewn up, just as with any operation on the living. Finally they are taken out of the theatre, sometimes to the recovery room, where relatives may still be waiting to say their final goodbyes. Otherwise, the body goes straight to the mortuary. The entire procedure may have taken up to three hours to perform.

The identity of the recipients is never revealed, even to me. Instead, a letter from the recipients' hospital gives a vague description of the people who have benefited, and how successful the transplants have been. It will also include a note of thanks from the Transplant Co-Ordinator, and copies of these letters are sent to the donor's relatives. These letters are very important to us. We sometimes feel that it is us who have to do the dirty work whilst it is the transplant team who get all the thanks.

Studies have been done to see if there is a lasting effect upon relatives who have agreed to donate the organs of someone they loved who had died. They show that most relatives derive a great deal of comfort from the act, that they feel that out of death has come life, although life for someone else. Knowing that others had benefited from the organs enabled them to feel that the patient's death had not been a complete waste, that they hadn't died for nothing.

Asking relatives for their permission to remove a patient's organs is a delicate business, and there are some times when we decide it would be inappropriate to raise the matter. Even though the patient would be an ideal donor, suggesting they consent to organ removal would cause just too much distress to relatives already close to breakdown. After a while doing the job, you develop a very good sense about which relatives will agree, and are therefore worth approaching, and those who are going to say no. Sometimes, this doesn't require much skill.

I remember one young girl, in her mid-teens, from a large Asian family, who was admitted to the Unit after being involved in a very serious car crash. She had suffered terrible head injuries, and I could see right from the start that there wasn't much chance she would live. We did our best, but she didn't respond, and I wasn't surprised when a first set of brain stem death tests showed no response. When a second set of tests confirmed that the brain stem was indeed irreversibly damaged we had no option but to declare her brain stem dead.

Her father completely refused to accept it. He was the patriarch of a large extended family, someone who was used to having his words treated as law, and he just could not believe that his daughter was dead. He could see her breathing with the help of a ventilator, the signal from her beating heart displayed on her monitor, and when he held he hand, it was still as soft and warm as if she were simply asleep. Despite what I had just told him, in his mind, she was still alive.

We tried again to explain what had happened, but he wouldn't listen. We told him all about the tests and how they had shown no response and what this meant, but it didn't make any difference. This was going to be difficult. I was surrounded by his family, and I could feel that some of them understood what I was

164

saying and agreed with me, but since their father was the boss, there weren't going to say anything. So, together with the nurse, I explained the whole procedure again.

Still we were getting nowhere. It was obvious that he was never going to accept the fact that his daughter had died, no matter what I said. Usually, I will devote whatever time is necessary to help relatives comes to terms with a brain stem death. It's an issue which needs to be approached and explained with care. However, this discussion had gone round in circles for well over an hour, and now it was time for action. If he had his way, that poor, dead little girl would remain on a ventilator for ever. I couldn't let that happen so I decided that it was time to take action.

There was no point in asking him for permission to remove his daughter's organs – he wouldn't even have contemplated the idea. So neither was there any point in keeping her hooked up to a ventilator for a moment longer. After one more futile attempt to persuade him that his daughter was dead, I decided to leave him and his family with a nurse in the relatives' waiting room – and simply turn off the ventilator myself.

As I got up to leave, however, he must have worked out what I was going to do. Immediately, there was a scuffle, and several sons ran past me as I walked back to the Intensive Care Unit, and surrounded the girl's bedside, refusing to let me near the ventilator. Everyone on the Unit looked up to see what was going on, and at the top of his voice, the father shouted, 'My daughter isn't dead. You're trying to murder my daughter. Keep away from that machine. You're not going to murder my girl.'

His words echoed all around the Unit, and I could see that relatives visiting patients in adjoining beds were deeply shocked and upset – they must have wondered what on earth was going on. Why was a doctor being accused of murder by an old man so obviously distressed? Once again, I told him about the brain stem tests, but he simply pointed to the monitor above her bed and said, 'Her heart is still going. Her chest is still moving. She is not dead.'

What could I do? Summoning porters to push past the family was out of the question, and would not have been the right way to settle such an important matter. Instead, I decided that the only course of action was to rely on the law of the land.

Death in this country is governed by strict legislation. Since the young girl's demise had been caused by a car crash, there would have to be an inquest held at a coroner's court. It would examine all of the reasons why the crash had occurred, and how the girl had sustained the injury which later killed her. Legally, that young girl's body had belonged to the coroner right from the moment the second set of tests had confirmed that she was dead, and had been certified as such by a doctor. So I decided to give the coroner a call.

I explained what had happened, and how I was being accused of murder. I told him that the family had surrounded the bedside and were refusing to see reason, and that I wasn't sure what I should do now. His reply was swift.

'Well, is she dead doctor?' he asked, and I replied that yes, she most certainly was. 'Right,' he replied. 'In that case switch off the ventilator immediately, and say that you have reported the case to me.' And our conversation ended.

Armed with the coroner's instructions, I immediately went back to the girl's bedside where the father and family were still keeping guard. This was not a time for pussyfooting around.

'I have spoken to the coroner,' I said, 'and he has instructed me to turn the machine off.' Without further ado, I walked past the sons, past the father and straight up to the ventilator.

When the silence came, her father collapsed in abject grief. No one had tried to stop me doing my duty, no one had punched me, and none of the threats had been carried out. Instead, when the ventilator stopped, the unavoidable fact that the young girl was really dead finally settled in and no one said a word.

Now, the entire family was beginning the process of grieving for a daughter who had died at too tender an age. Looking around me, at the old man in tears and all of the faces by her bedside, I felt nothing but sorrow and sympathy. Later, as I was walking down the corridor outside the Unit, I saw one of her brothers coming the other way. I could not avoid meeting him. As we drew close to one another he put out his hand to shake mine. 'Thank you, doctor. Please thank all the other doctors and nurses. We know that everything possible was done to save my sister. We loved her so much and she was looked after so beautifully, right up to the end.'

Imagine in your mind's eye the face of the person you love most out of all of the people on this earth. Then imagine what you would say if you knew you only had half an hour or maybe less before you walked away from them for the last time? What would you tell them? Would it be your hopes and dreams for the future and the bitterness that they would never be fulfilled? Would it be the happiness of shared experiences, the intimate moments, a simple love, and a celebration of life and times together? Or would it be the agony of regret for things said or done and the knowledge of how time had run out before amends could be made?

All of these things are felt and said by the relatives we see on this Intensive Care Unit. Merely watching a parent cuddle for the last time the warm body of a child who was once alive but is now dead can be a harrowing experience. I remember once one father wanted to hold his young son, free of all the medical apparatus which had surrounded his bed from the moment he had been admitted to the Unit after a serious car smash. He wanted to cuddle the boy and remember the lad's face without a tube leading from the ventilator into his lungs, and lines from the monitor attached to various parts of his body. Yet he knew that this couldn't be done because he had agreed that his son should be an organ donor, and switching off the ventilator would reduce the oxygen saturation of the blood, damaging the very organs we were trying to save. In the end, we disconnected the ventilator for a short while, feeding pure oxygen down the endotracheal tube to make up the deficit, allowing the father time to see his boy as he had always seen him before the accident. Then, after just a few minutes, we had no option but to reconnect the machine.

It was all that the man had wanted, a memory of his son as a normal young lad, seeing for the last time a face which he had often kissed good night in previous years. He held his hand, and talked to him; he spoke of all the things they had done together, and how he had cherished great hopes for the boy, right from the moment of his birth. He said all the things he had always wanted to say but felt he never could because men often feel they cannot speak to each other, not even a father to his son. After one last hug, he turned and walked away. The boy was just sixteen years old.

A Final Word

AT THE END OF IT ALL, after a successful struggle to save a life, after all of the specialist medical techniques, and the care and attention lavished unsparingly by the staff, what does the patient remember about their stay on the Intensive Care Unit?

What do they recall about the day they were admitted, the frantic attempts to keep them alive long enough to be able to treat them at all, the continual assessment, the monitors, the machines, the injections and the relatives waiting anxiously around their bed? In short, what do they remember about their time at the centre of all this drama, the time everyone thought they were going to die?

The answer is surprisingly simple. They usually remember absolutely nothing – not a day, nor an hour, nor a minute. Most will have been unconscious for the entire time, before moving to another ward as their recovery continued. They don't remember any of the names of the people who treated them, not even their faces. It has become a merciful blank.

Yet some still come back to say thank you. They don't recognise any of the staff, and we can barely recognise them, free from tubes and bandages, and dressed in ordinary clothes. In many ways, it is a meeting between strangers, and a slight awkwardness sometimes pervades the occasion. Standing in front of us is a normal, healthy human being, far removed from the desperately ill patient that we knew. Here, in front of us, is someone who could have died but has lived. Here, in front of us, is the undeniable fruit of our labours.